MR. PRONE

A Week in the Life of an Ignorant Man

C. H. ROLPH

MR. PRONE

A Week in the Life of an Ignorant Man

ILLUSTRATED BY
DAVID ENGLISH

OXFORD   LONDON   NEW YORK
OXFORD UNIVERSITY PRESS
1977

Oxford University Press, Walton Street, Oxford OX2 6DP

OXFORD LONDON GLASGOW
NEW YORK TORONTO MELBOURNE WELLINGTON
IBADAN NAIROBI DAR ES SALAAM LUSAKA CAPE TOWN
KUALA LUMPUR SINGAPORE JAKARTA HONG KONG TOKYO
DELHI BOMBAY CALCUTTA MADRAS KARACHI

© C. H. ROLPH 1977

British Library Cataloguing in Publication Data

Rolph, C. H.
  Mr Prone.
  1. Law – England
  I. Title
  340′.0942   KD662   77–30094
  ISBN 0–19–212966–X

*Printed in Great Britain by
Billing and Sons, Ltd,
Guildford, London, and Worcester*

Foreword

Almost everything in this story that the Law of England inflicts upon the unhappy and incredulous Mr. Prone could happen to any one of us; and anyone who, like Mr. Prone, keeps a newsagent's and general shop can leave out the almost. Let it be admitted that so many mishaps would be unlikely, according to the theories of probability and statistical frequency, to befall one man in the course of a single week, or indeed a single lifetime. But a dramatic convenience has been made of Mr. Prone, so that he may stand between us and The Law. If anyone, reading here of his shifts and follies, grows at all in rectitude and wisdom—no one will be more surprised than myself.

C. H. ROLPH

Contents

That was the Week

IF you were one of those who claim to know what a criminal looks like, you could have been forgiven for holding that, on this particular Saturday afternoon, Mr. Prone looked like a criminal. The magistrates' court was one of those in which the accused person, if he is merely there in answer to a summons, stands (or even sits) in front of a 'dock' or cage and is called a defendant; while if he is already in custody he stands (or more rarely sits) inside it. Mr. Prone stood inside it. He had spent part of the Friday night in a police-station cell, sleepless, collarless, without shoelaces or the means of keeping his trousers up (the police always believe that these may be used by prisoners as a means of hanging themselves), and crushed with incredulity that it should be he, of all men, who had played the leading role in the events of That Week; events of which this had been the outrageous culmination. As we meet him in this chapter, he is unshaven, depersonalized, hollow-eyed and sullen (he had been too sullen to shave). So even if he had been allowed to stand or sit in front of the dock, he would still have looked like a man from whom you would not lightly buy a second-hand car.

'Percival Prone,' said the chairman of the magistrates, 'my colleagues and I have decided—'

'I want Legal Aid', said Mr. Prone.

There was a pause.

'Perhaps you had better be quiet for a minute', the magistrate went on. 'I was about to tell you—'

'And I want to be tried by a jury.'

'You *have* suddenly found your voice, haven't you? You've given us very little help until now. I had better remind you that you were asked at the beginning of this hearing whether you wanted to be tried by jury on the charge of possessing a housebreaking implement, and you said that you consented to the jurisdiction of this court. Since then you have said nothing.'

'I'm not talking about that', said Mr. Prone doggedly. 'I mean the other business, about me being a suspected person and intending to commit some sort of crime. That's all made up, that is; whereas the other thing, well, if a screwdriver's what you call a housebreaking implement, I had it with me didn't I? I've often got it with me. It's the suspected person business I won't have, and I want that gone into by a jury, not you.'

At this point the justices' clerk sat up straight. Neither he nor anyone there could know that this was a new Mr. Prone, an overwrought one, the product of the worst week ever arranged for one of its protégés by the English legal system.

'You have pleaded Not Guilty to both charges,' said the justices' clerk, 'and all the evidence has now been heard.'

'Not mine it hasn't', said the wrathful Mr. Prone, who, truth to tell, barely recognized himself in this extraordinary scene. 'I've got a lot to say about this, but I want Legal Aid first.'

'You could have asked for Legal Aid from the start. You didn't do so. Nevertheless you would have been offered Legal Aid if the magistrates had thought, at the end of the police evidence, that you needed professional defence—'

'I *did* ask for it from the start. I told the police last night I wanted Legal Aid, I wanted a solicitor called. I've got a solicitor who knows all about me, but he's gone away. They said I couldn't get Legal Aid until

I was in front of the magistrates, and now it's Saturday afternoon and you won't find a solicitor anywhere. Now what I say is this: if I was a rich man I could have got my solicitor last night—'

The chairman thumped his desk with Volume Three of *Stone's Justices' Manual*. 'Will you listen to me', he roared, and a silence fell. 'We have considered this case with great care, and we have sat late into a Saturday afternoon to do so. We think you are ill-advised to take your dog out at night without putting its collar on, or at least without keeping it on a chain or strap. We think you acted incautiously in entering someone else's garden in search of it. We have decided to attach no importance to the fact that no such dog was seen by anyone at the time of your arrest. We accept the dog. It may be your habit, as you say, to wear plimsolls on your nightly walks, but that is also the chosen footwear of many others who, partly because of it, have stood in that dock. It may be that, as a home handyman, you would often have a screwdriver in your pocket. It may be that pride, and solicitude for your wife and family, would lead you to withhold your name and address from the police for so long, and thus delay your admission to bail. All these things taken together, however, look very odd, and much of the blame for what has happened rests with yourself. The police have told us that it was not until after midnight that you gave them your name. But for a mischance, that belated decision might well have been enough to clear you, for you are well known to the police at your local station as a hitherto respectable shopkeeper. But you happen to live on a police divisional boundary, and you seem to prefer exercising your dog within the police division whose station is three miles away, and where you are not known. We feel that a doubt exists in this case, and we have decided that you should be given the benefit of such doubt as there is—'

'Doubt?' gasped the angry Mr. Prone. 'What doubt? Benefit of what doubt? I'm not having that. I'm either guilty or I'm innocent. Not doubtful. I want my name cleared and I demand to go before a judge and jury on this charge of being, what is it, a Suspected Person Loitering—'

'You could not be committed for trial on that particular charge,' interrupted the magistrates' clerk, 'even if there were enough evidence against you. It's one that no jury can deal with. And in fact you won't be committed for trial at all. The magistrates have found you Not Guilty. What are you grumbling about?'

'They haven't said so, have they?' snorted Mr. Prone. 'Doubtful, that's what they said. They think I might have done it but they're not sure enough. Great, isn't it? Well, I didn't do it. I didn't do anything wrong at all, and I want that stated in open court and in the newspapers—'

'Mr. Prone, we can't—'

'And I want Legal Aid and a barrister and a proper trial.'

'Mr. Prone,' said the chairman very deliberately, 'we have found you not guilty and you are discharged.'

'This way', said the court jailer, a man accustomed to showing people which way.

Mr. Prone gripped the dock rail and prepared to deliver his peroration. The jailer took his arm, and he shook himself free.

'I want to make a statement.'

The chairman leaned over to whisper with the clerk, shrugged, and settled back with a glance at the clock. 'You have not been at any disadvantage by not being represented,' he said, 'but we don't want you to *think* you have, though you have declined to say much until now. If you have something you now wish to say, please make it short.'

Mr. Prone produced a crumpled sheet of paper from his pocket and cleared his throat.

'Shorter than that', said the chairman, who knew these sheets of paper.

'After all that's been happening to me this week,' began Mr. Prone, 'I have lost my faith in this country, and the police, and the courts, and democracy. And everything. There used to be freedom here, or I used to believe there was, and justice and all. But now you go out for a short walk at night to give the dog a run, just round the houses, and what happens? You're arrested and questioned and bullied and called a liar, and they want your fingerprints, and you're kept in a locked cell. And nobody cares. There's no Public Defender or nobody you can get a message to. You hear a lot about the Public Prosecutor, oh yes, we all know about him. What about a Public Defender? That's what we need. Well, I'm going to take this further myself. You haven't heard the last of this. . . .'

Mr. Prone folded up his paper. 'I've got a bit more here,' he said, 'but I'll save it up, it's just wasted here. I'll just say one other thing. I'm not satisfied with you saying I get the "benefit of the doubt". I don't know whether you're a crook or a twister,' he said to the chairman, 'and you wouldn't be the first one on the Bench if you was. But seeing as I don't know, do I give you the benefit of the doubt? No, I say, "OK, you're not a crook", not "Well, he might be, mightn't he, but I suppose I haven't heard enough about him"—'

'Leave the court please', said the justices' clerk. 'Officer, remove him from the court.'

'Hang on—I haven't finished yet, have I?' said Mr. Prone. 'This case might seem to *you* to be all over, but it means a lot more to me than what it does to you, and I say it isn't over yet.' He cast an eye towards the press seats, where at long last one very young lady and a middle-aged and obviously staunch inebriate had begun to write in their books. 'I want to know a lot about this. I want to know—'

'Come along now, that'll be about enough', said the court jailer.

'Just one moment', the chairman said suddenly. 'Perhaps you could be quiet for one more moment, Mr. Prone. Is the police officer here?'

A CID man stepped forward.

'Sir?'

'Did the question of bail arise when he was first arrested?'

'Bail, your Worship? He didn't give any address.'

'But I suppose you took his personal property from his pockets before putting him in a cell?'

'Yes, your Worship.'

'Did that include no diary or letters or memos from which you could find out who he was?'

'No, sir, nothing at all.'

'Did his behaviour seem at all odd to you last night? Was he abusive or difficult?'

'Very *much* so, your worship. He had to be restrained at times. He was shouting a lot, and actually he picked up a book and threw it at the station officer.'

'Hit him?'

'No sir, it missed.'

'You've made no mention of that this afternoon?'

'Well no, sir. We hadn't charged him with disorderly behaviour in the police station. We didn't think—'

'How did he behave during detention?'

'Oh very noisy, sir. Shouting most of the time, and he refused any food.'

'No food?'

'None sir.'

'I suppose no doctor has seen him?'

'Doctor sir? No sir.'

'You probably see what's in my mind, officer? I'm rather disturbed now about his mental state, to be plain.'

'Well there *is* rather a story behind it all, sir. I think what's been happening to Mr. Prone this week *may* have unhinged his mind a little. It's nothing to do with this case this afternoon, sir, but it is a pretty odd story—'

But at this point Mr. Prone could listen no longer.

'Oh, that's about all I need', he shouted. 'You can't give me just ordinary, simple justice, and when I demand it you turn round and say I must be potty to ask for it. That's rich, that is, that's a drop of real gravy. Well, I'm just as sane as you are, see?' he told the chairman. 'I'm no more mad than anyone here, and if you're going to start that talk—'

'Listen', said the chairman once again. 'I am trying to decide whether you are really fit to take care of yourself, fit to manage your own affairs, and I have it in mind to suggest that you might seek psychiatric help.'

'That's just what I thought. And then shut me up again? That's it, isn't it? That's what I call rich. If you can't get me on one thing, you get me on another. Blimey, this might as well be Russia, it's just the kind of thing you hear about. Look, I'm all right, see, I just don't like being arrested and locked up for something I haven't done—'

And as Mr. Prone continued with the defence of his impugned sanity, the chairman watched him fixedly, with his face cupped in his hands.

'Very well', he said at last. 'I think you had better go.'

And Mr. Prone went. As he descended the stairs to recover his 'property', he noticed that among the people sitting around the court-room (who *were* all these people?—there always seemed to be idlers who could just sit around and supply the unhappiest of landscapes with figures) there was Mr. Goodenough, who kept the off-licence in Spenser Road and whom he did not like. Mr. Goodenough was there to answer a summons for speeding, but Mr. Prone supposed at once that he had somehow got to know about the affair of the dog, the plimsolls, and the screwdriver, and was there to gloat. Mr. Goodenough greeted his hapless neighbour with an objectionably cheerful thumbs-up sign, but neither of Mr. Prone's thumbs responded.

Percival Prone was a hard-working, busy, and discriminatingly law-abiding corner-shop newsagent. In a few years he had turned No. 84 Spenser Road, South London, into one of those 'urban village' oases which, as the London suburban shop-leases fall in, and the rents and the encroaching tower-blocks reach the sky, are now inspiring wistful nostalgia. This was partly because, either through ignorance of the Sunday trading laws or in public-spirited defiance of them, his shop had become widely known as a place where you could buy almost anything on a Sunday that you had run out of. Indeed people almost deliberately ran out of things in order to have reason to go there, and at about midday every Sunday the little shop was crowded with the systematically forgetful. Tinned foods and jams, cakes and eggs, milk and butter and cheese —an endless variety of demands.

As we enter with him upon the memorable Week that was to admit his name to the noble army of martyrs, he was 45, active, sober, tubby, kindly, quick-witted, small, and bespectacled. To compensate for a saucer-sized patch of bare skull, Nature had decently permitted him a tentative growth of sideburns. He belonged to things: to the Chamber of Commerce, to the National Federation of Retail Newsagents, to the Special Constabulary, to the Liberal Party. The little time left over from his daily round—a phrase which must be understood as including football pool entries, various competitions offering holidays in Spain, and do-it-yourself home maintenance—was spent in shortish periods of impassive torpor before his television set.

No. 84 stood at a London suburban cross-roads. The four roads meeting there were not busy, but they were permanently lined on both sides with parked cars which left grudging gaps at the few places where the residents and shopkeepers had garage entrances—and of these Percival Prone, Newsagent, Tobacconist, and General Stores, was one. Diagonally opposite No. 84 was the Rose and Crown, whose hard-drinking patrons were largely also Mr. Prone's; but he was not a pub man. Beer, wines, and spirits were not important to him; mainly because, as he would explain to enquirers, 80 per cent of their cost went straight to the government in taxes, and there had never in his lifetime been a government which, as a Liberal, he approved of and would voluntarily support. To anyone who reminded him that, as a pipe-smoker, he paid more than 80 per cent of his tobacco costs to governments he disliked, he retorted that the tax on tobacco was a diabolical liberty.

Mrs. Prone was a small, sharp-featured wife in whom Mr. Prone was very lucky. He knew he was, though her devotion found alternating expression in solicitude, abuse, and the rather shrill indulgence of reproachful hindsight. You could not have said that she helped in the shop. She was so energetic and efficient that it was really Mr. Prone who helped in the shop. She was up at five every week-day, winter and summer, to make the early morning tea, count the morning newspapers, pencil on them the names of their supporters, and arrange for their delivery by the newsboys. She arranged the display counter outside the shop, filled the two children with porridge, bacon, and tomatoes, and dispatched them to school.

Their names were Susan and James. Susan, at 15 a non-studious and uncomplaining girl, was in dogged and unquestioning pursuit of O-levels in eight subjects. If ever she asked what life was all about, she addressed the question to herself in the strictest privacy. It was an odd life, but she got on with it. James, a smallish boy for his nine years, had mapped out for himself a career as a professional footballer, in which book-learning at all levels was expected to think itself lucky to be allotted a minor part. By way of a beginning, he played at inside-left when the local Methodist Church, in which he worshipped at infrequent intervals, fielded a team in Spenser Park at the top of the road. And Mr. Prone, once a passable footballer himself and now known to cherish a similar hope for his son, took every opportunity to coach him. Few Sunday afternoons went by without the involvement of Prone and Son in a football match of some kind.

The Prone family were little known as a family. Prone's was a shop; and the nature of it brought neighbourhood people together in gossipy circumstances. Anything that happened to Mr. Prone happened also to the 'village', was endured by it, enjoyed, resented, or discussed as a common experience. He was not a man who knew much about the law, apart from what he had casually learned from his trade magazine and in the course of vaguely worrying visits from Shops Act inspectors. If he had been but reasonably conversant with the law, this history would not have come to be written. And although he had heard it said that 'ignorance of the law is no excuse', he found that much of it seemed so absurd and unreasonable that to be ignorant of it suggested a kind of sagacity, a feeling of otherness which, without hurt to one's self-respect, might well be called ignorance. 'If that's the law, I don't want to know about it.' Mr. Prone was a consciously, and some might have said a blissfully, ignorant man.

Sunday

PERCIVAL PRONE, Newsagent and Tobacconist, proprietor of the Spenser Park General Stores, didn't worry about an early closing day. He was aware that the law[1] allowed him to stay open on *any* week-day until 8.00 in the evening to sell his newspapers and his magazines, and until 9.30 to sell his tobacco, cigarettes, and confectionery. And that on one evening a week, by some mysterious indulgence of Parliament, he could go on selling his confectionery until 10 o'clock. He had never quite understood why the law should take no interest, though he was grateful that it didn't, in what time he started work in the mornings, which was usually about half-past five. And he had often remarked to

[1] Shops Act 1950 (First Schedule).

Mrs. Prone that, for all the law cared, their shop could open every
day at a minute after midnight. 'You would be opening it on your
own if it did,' she would say, 'and you would stay on your own until
I got up.'

But on Sundays the law was more interested in what Mr. Prone sold
in his shop than in the times at which he sold it. On Sunday mornings
the Prones had a lie-in. Moreover, it was on the Sabbath that he went
downstairs and made the tea, and this did not occur until half-past
seven. By that time the parcels of Sunday papers had (by long arrangement) been dumped in his garage by the distributors' vans, and the
Lord's Day could be said to have stirred itself into movement. All over
Great Britain this would happen at widely differing times but with a
striking similarity of behaviour, as millions of forearms emerged fur-
tively from partly-opened front doors to grasp, first, a bottle of milk,
and then one or more of the competing Sunday papers. It was commonly held that this was the moment at which the citizens of Britain
began an essential (and illustrated) weekly tutorial in the ways of the
world, the flesh, and the devil. The Sunday routine of the Prones was
essential to its continuation.

It was at 10.15 a.m. on a dull Sunday in November that a more percipient retail trader than Mr. Prone would have recognized the first sign of
trouble. A man had come in to buy the *News of the World*, pocketed his
change, put the folded paper under his arm, and stood looking through
the *Sunday People* in such a manner as to suggest that his thoughts were
elsewhere. Mr. Prone and his wife were bustling about, serving other
customers with the usual variety of goods. Cigarettes and tobacco, newspapers, tins of milk, eggs, bread, a packet of cornflakes, a cabbage, an
electric light battery, a little plastic bag of potatoes, an occasional paperback. Mr. Prone had just sold a packet of playing cards to Mrs. French,
the barmaid from the Rose and Crown across the way, when the man
looking through the *Sunday People* suddenly put it neatly back in its
place and came across to him.

'I am an Inspector under the Shops Act,' he said, 'and I have just
seen you sell this lady a pack of playing cards. Here is my authority. The
law does not allow you to sell that kind of thing on a Sunday.'

And to Mrs. French's temporarily speechless indignation he then
took the guilty packet from the top of her shopping basket. 'Would you
kindly give me your name and address, madam?' he said to her.

'I shall do no such thing', she retorted, and snatched the little parcel
from him. 'And if you want a pack of cards you can buy one yourself.'

Mrs. French strode angrily from the shop and the little parcel went with her.

Now the Shops Act Inspector *could* have bought one for himself while he was buying his *News of the World*; but indignation about that kind of thing had been filling the correspondence pages of the local paper for many months. There is no more hated figure on the British legal landscape than the official who provokes or instigates a breach of the law in order to get it punished: the *agent provocateur*—we will not even give him a British name. No one seems very fond, for that matter, of Shops Act Inspectors, who are widely (and unfairly) regarded not merely as dismal Jimmies but as *agents provocateurs* of the meanest kind. But when local grocers complained to the police and to the Borough Council (as they often did) that Mr. Prone was profiting at their expense because he broke the law and they didn't, something had to be done.[1]

'Well,' said Mr. Prone with a carefully simulated air of bewilderment, 'what *can* I sell on a Sunday? This is something I've never been clear about and I don't know anybody who is.'

Obligingly, it may be thought, the Inspector handed him a printed list of the things he could lawfully sell. It seemed enormous; it seemed unreasonable not to be satisfied with such thoughtful and particularized scope—each item, no doubt, the final result of much debate, lobbying, petitioning, and objection; and yet, it seemed to Mr. Prone, most of the things on it were not goods or services for which you would go to Mr. Prone. We shall consider some of them in a moment.

'I shall have to report this,' the Inspector was saying in a formal voice, 'with a view to prosecuting you under the Shops Act 1950 for opening this shop on a Sunday for a purpose other than a transaction mentioned on that list.'

When he had gone, the remaining customers gathered round for an impromptu indignation meeting. The Prones, it was agreed, were providing a much-needed public service by opening on a Sunday at all. Compulsory Sunday observance was a lot of rot. Why, it reminded you of the days when you could be burned at the stake for going to the wrong church. They ordered these things better on the Continent:

[1] The law itself did not lack supporters, and never has. On 11 February 1976, for example, Sir John Langford-Holt, Tory M.P. for Shrewsbury, tried to change it for the benefit of people like Mr. Prone by means of a Private Member's Bill. He was concerned for the time being only with week-day early closing. But on behalf of the Union of Shop, Distributive and Allied Workers Mr. Torney, Labour member for Bradford South, said they had always been the Cinderellas of industry, working 'long and unsocial hours'; and they would oppose the Bill. Did anyone suppose that the big firms in the High Street would be willing to lose cash while owner-occupied businesses opened at any hour? The Bill was defeated by 159 votes to 151.

perhaps the Common Market would put an end to all this nonsense? The one dissentient, a man whom nobody seemed to know (and would anyone wish to know such a man?), said that Sunday closing represented a hard-won right on the part of shop assistants, and that people like the Prones *could* be seen as lawbreakers getting away with conduct forbidden to decent people who happened to employ shop assistants. And this man was just going on to point out, in a God-preserve-us-from-the-Continental-Sunday sort of voice, that a shop assistant anyway could be a member of the shopkeeper's own family, perhaps his own son or daughter, even if they got no pay, when the shop door opened and there entered a tall policeman. Mr. Prone peered at the policeman over his glasses. 'Oh NO!' he said, with the inhospitable inflection to which policemen grow accustomed.

'Good morning', said the policeman. He took off his helmet and dusted it with the sleeve of his greatcoat. Then he held it at arm's length for inspection. 'That's been rolling in the mud,' he said accusingly, 'and do you know why? Because your shop-blind outside is too low. Knocked it clean off as I turned the corner.'

'Couldn't have bin lookin' where 'e was goin',' muttered a man waiting to buy cigarettes. He spoke without looking round and may have been just thinking aloud; but it was the general feeling afterwards that his interjection, fair enough on the face of it perhaps, may have done Mr. Prone little good. (A policeman is trained never to turn a corner without looking back, especially on those occasions, now rare, when he is walking and not riding in a car. It is a precaution known in some police areas as 'the ole Lot's wife'. Someone may be distantly trying to attract his attention from the road he is just about to leave; or someone in that road may be equally but criminally anxious *not* to attract his attention at all. But the looking-back can be mistimed: it should follow, not precede, a quick look into the street he has just arrived at. Police Constable Flynn's timing was wrong and the mishap therefore partly his own fault; but the law[1] makes no allowance for that.)

'That awning ought to be at least eight feet from the ground', the policeman told Mr. Prone. 'Are you the person responsible?'

'Well, it's my shop', said Mr. Prone.

'Your shop-awning isn't much more than six feet from the ground. I want you to give me your full name, please, and I shall report you for a summons.'

'I'm not giving my name to anyone', Mr. Prone said desperately. 'Where is all this going to end? If you want my full name you can find it out.'

[1] Town Police Clauses Act 1847.

'O.K., I can probably do that. You'll have your full name over the shop door, won't you, outside? One-inch white letters, "licensed to sell tobacco", etc.? I'll just have a look before we go any further.'

Mr. Prone shot a panic-stricken look at his wife as the policeman went to the door and opened it. 'We've never had it done again', he whispered. 'After you having this green paint everywhere, we never had the letters put back.'

'Me?' Mrs. Prone almost hissed. 'Has this one got to be my fault then? Why, that's eleven years ago we had the painting done. No one's ever said anything about the letters not being painted up there till today.'

The policeman came back. 'I see you haven't got your full name over the door, as required by law,' he said, 'you being a retailer of tobacco. I'm afraid I shall have to report you for that too.'

Mr. Prone shrugged. 'Percival Prone', he said.

His mind may have been partly informed about the intricacies of Sunday trading restriction, but it was totally and genuinely uninformed about the prescribed height of shop awnings. This one was a complete surprise to him. A surprise was on its way for the policeman, too, in the matter of the name over a tobacconist's door; but for the moment their joint concern was the shop awning.

'It's not many years since I had that put up', he said. 'It keeps the rain off my news-stand outside there, on a week-day, I don't use it of a Sunday. The bloke who put it up never said anything about eight feet.'

'And did he put it up the way it is now?' asked the policeman.

'Yes. I don't know. It may have worked loose and drooped a bit.'

'In any case I'm afraid you're the man responsible. What was that you said about a news-stand?'

'Well, I always put out a show of papers and magazines on that, of a weekday. Not Sundays. People like to pick up their newspaper without coming in the shop, people hurrying along on their way to the station mostly. Anything wrong with that?'

'Have you got some kind of permit to stand that on the public highway?'

'Permit? No. What d'you mean, permit? We've all got that kind of stall along here, or a lot of us have. The Do-It-Yourself Shop, the Gardening Centre, the junk shop along there, the greengrocer, we've all got them.'

'And do you know something, all of you are obstructing the footway unlawfully? You'd better take it in, right now.'

'What! I can't move *that*. It's made of old floorboards and heavy quartering and I should think it weighs about a ton. I never attempt to move it.'

'Oh? So it's a *permanent* structure on the highway? A building really, you might say. I'm afraid I shall have to report that for another summons.'[1]

'Oh come off it, mate, there's been a stall of some kind out there for donkeys' years—there was certainly one when I came here. I reckon I've got a right to that: if it goes on for long enough without the law interfering, well then you get a right to it, a right to go on using it. What are *you* after, promotion or something?'

'I think you're going to find all these footway obstructions have got to be moved. If you put something like that out there, and nothing happens about it for any number of years, that doesn't give you any licence to go on doing it.[2] That's an old wives' tale. A lot of people think it does but they're wrong.'

There was a pause while this very confident-seeming policeman wrote rather slowly in a little book.

'Is that all?' said Mr. Prone bitterly.

'I haven't actually told you what I came in for, have I?' the policeman said, almost like a guest who has forgotten his manners. 'Do you employ a boy named James Prone?'

'Employ him? That's my son.'

'He delivers papers for you?'

'What? He does, yes. On Saturdays and Sundays he does as a rule. Not weekdays, I've got another boy for weekdays.'

'And how old is your son, Mr. Prone?'

Mr. Prone thought rapidly.

'He's thirteen,' he said, 'soon be fourteen.'

'Now I wonder which is right. When I met him earlier this morning he said he'd be ten on 10 January.'

'Why did you want to know? Did you stop him in the street? When was this?'

'Well, it was still dark and he had no lights on his bicycle, Mr. Prone. That's why I stopped him.'

Mr. Prone called to his wife. 'Would you believe this?' he demanded rhetorically. 'Jimmy went out this morning without any lights on that bike, after all I've said to him. Didn't I tell him to ask you for new batteries?'

It was the policeman who replied. 'That boy had no lamps on his bicycle. Batteries wouldn't have been much good to him, would they? I'm afraid this means you're involved as the employer, permitting the boy to commit the offence.'

---

[1] Highways Act 1959, section 121, or Town Police Clauses Act 1847, section 28.

[2] *Redbridge London Borough* v. *Jacques* (1971), 1 All E.R. 260.

'Employer?' said Mr. Prone again. 'I tell you he's my son. I'm his father, not his employer, he doesn't draw wages.'

'It seems you're both. And you see it doesn't make any difference even if you pay him nothing. He's helping you in a trade carried on for profit, so the law says you're employing him.'[1]

By this time the little shop was crowded with Sunday customers waiting to be served. There were more of them than Mrs. Prone could cope with. 'James', she called. 'Jimmy, haven't you finished your breakfast? Come on, I want you in the shop.'

James, a small wiry boy, appeared at the door with his mouth full.

'O.K. Mum', he said, and then his face fell as he saw the policeman. 'I told him I was only ten', he muttered to his mother.

'We've met before, haven't we?' the policeman said. 'Mr. Prone, I was just about to say that I have to report you to the Education Authority for employing a child under the age of thirteen to deliver newspapers. I didn't know he served in the shop as well. Sort of strengthens the case, doesn't it?'

When the policeman had gone there was a second little indignation meeting of customers. This, it was generally agreed, was persecution. The Prones and their Sunday service were public benefactors. There was talk of petitions on their behalf to the Commissioner of Police, to the local authority, to their Member of Parliament, to the Home Secretary, to the Queen.

Thoughtfully at one o'clock Mr. Prone bolted the shop door, turned round the hanging card so that it should say CLOSED, in which position it looked unfamiliar and ill-at-ease, and prepared his mind with less than the usual relish for Sunday dinner. On this his wife and daughter had been bestowing odd moments of attention throughout the morning. As they sat round the table, the four of them, it became apparent that they all did so with impaired appetites.

'I could understand any one of them things happening to anyone who keeps a shop,' Mr. Prone said, holding his knife and fork upright on the table. 'But not all of them on the same morning, all in an hour, I can't hardly believe it.'

'Does it mean we don't open on a Sunday any more?' said Susan hopefully.

'No it does *not*. It means I can supply, well, only certain things.'

'What things, for instance?' said Mrs. Prone.

'Well, actually you never saw such a list. He gave me a list, it's

[1] Children and Young Persons Act 1933, section 18.

headed *Shops Act 1950, Fifth Schedule, Restrictions on Sunday Trading*. It says I can sell intoxicants—'

'What!' Mrs. Prone was in favour of selling beer and wine, and her husband was not. 'We can't, can we? Not without a licence?'

'No, that's meant for pubs and off-licences. No doubt we could get an off-licence if we tried. If I did I could sell wine and beer on a Sunday anyway. Not spirits. Anyway I don't want any of that. As it is, we can sell meals or refreshments, but we can't be a fish-and-chip shop—'

'It doesn't really *say* fish-and-chip shop?'

'Oh yes it does. And we can sell newly cooked provisions—and that includes bread, it seems; and "cooked or partly cooked tripe", what do you know about that?'

'Why?'

'Why what?'

'Partly cooked?'

'I suppose some people like a sort of instant-tripe Sunday dinner, just warm it up in five minutes. Then I can sell table waters—'

'What are they?'

'Mineral waters, I suppose; we sell them anyway. And sweets and chocolates and sugar confectionery (I suppose they're all different in some way); and ice cream in wafers or cones. And then flowers, fresh fruit and vegetables, but not any kind of tinned stuff. Fresh milk and cream—and it says the cream *can* be in tins if it's clotted, now there's a brain-wave, there's democracy for you. So it goes on. Medicine and bandages. Aircraft accessories, that's useful, that is: fat lot of those we could sell here. Motor and cycle supplies. Passport photographs, that's another laugh.'

'But we can sell those bats and balls? They said it was all right when we bought them?'

'All right to what? Sell them on Sundays? No one ever said anything about that, why should they? It says here the only people allowed to sell any kind of sports things on a Sunday are the shops at the places where the sport's carried on.'

'Where's that then?' said Mrs. Prone.

'I suppose,' volunteered James scornfully, 'if there was a Wembley Cup Final on a Sunday, and they lost their ball, they could buy a new one at the shop in Wembley Stadium.'

'You can always buy bats and balls and things on Sunday at the seaside,' said Susan, 'I remember because we've done it, and buckets and spades too.'

'I think there's a special law about buckets and spades in holiday places,' Mr. Prone said, 'but I don't know about bats and balls. I sold a pair of roller skates a couple of Sundays ago, remember? I suppose that's wrong because this is not a skating rink.'

'Oh nonsense, they were second-hand, an old pair of Jimmy's', said Mrs. Prone.

'Makes no difference. I'm ready to believe anything now', Mr. Prone said. 'I don't know what to think about all them paperbacks in the rack. It says here we can only sell those, and books and stationery, if we're running a bookstall at a railway station or a bus terminal or an airport. Well, we're not. Oh, and we could sell guide books and picture postcards and souvenirs if we were an ancient monument. Or a museum or gallery or public park or zoo. Great, isn't it? Every time we sell a paperback novel on a Sunday, or even a rubber ball, we can be fined, what is it, £50. And then every rubber ball after that, £200. How many people know about all this, I wonder?'

Mrs. Prone was a practical woman, to whom a spade was not a rubber ball.

'The trouble about us,' she said, 'we've never bothered to find out. Never mind about what other people know. We *could* have found out from the Town Hall or somewhere. That's where we've been wrong, we just didn't *want* to know. Useless pretending we didn't know there was *some* rules about it all. Come on, you two, you can help me clear up while Dad gets the shop ready for five o'clock.' The Prones had been finding it worth while to open from five to seven on Sunday evenings.

James was dismayed. 'Oh look Mum, he was going to play football with me in Spenser Park. Just half an hour. It'll be dark if we don't go now. Please, Mum.'

'Oh all right, then, if he said so. Off you go.'

Twenty minutes later in Spenser Park Mr. Prone was surrounded by boys of the kind who, in any public park, will materialize from nowhere at the sight of a brand new football with only two people to kick it. Sides were picked, folded coats were put down to mark goal extremities, and the usual Sunday afternoon kickabout began.

It was never the kind of match that attracted spectators, or caused even the most rudderless of passers-by to stop passing by. And yet after ten minutes Mr. Prone, who was referee, became uneasily aware that the occasion was being intently watched by a man wearing a long overcoat, a long face, and a cloth cap, who from time to time took out his watch and looked at it. Although he contemplated the players and the ball without the smallest sign of approval, he seemed patient, waiting for something. And then a park-keeper appeared. At once the spectator went into action; and after he and the keeper had exchanged a few words, they jointly approached Mr. Prone.

'Excuse me', said the park-keeper to Mr. Prone, and the panting footballers gathered round. 'This gentleman has complained to me about you playing football here on a Sunday—'

'WHAT!' almost screamed Mr. Prone. 'Why, there's organized football matches over there all day on a Sunday, every Sunday, a dozen of 'em all going on at a time. Look, mate, they're playing now.'

'Yes, yes, I know all about that. I've told him that's perfectly lawful but he doesn't seem satisfied, even about that. He's asked me to get your name and address and he intends to take proceedings against you.'

'Take proceedings? What for?'

The man in the long overcoat spoke for the first time. 'This park-keeper has tried to tell me there's no objection now to Sunday football, but thank *God* there will always be some of us who will object to the public playing of games on the Sabbath. Are these boys members of a club?'

'Not so far as I know', said Mr. Prone. 'One of them's my son. Who are you, may I ask?'

'He's given me his name', the park-keeper said. 'He says he's a private citizen who wants the law enforced. He's talking about a Sunday Observance Act of 1625, but I believe that's all been repealed. I've got all about it in my rule-book here, I'll tell you in a moment.'

'There's been no repeal to my knowledge', said the man in the long overcoat primly. 'It's against the law of the land for any party of people to play football or cricket or any other game (except archery) outside their own parishes on a Sunday. I simply want to know whether this gentleman and these boys live in the Parish of St. Saviour's.'

The park-keeper surfaced again. 'I'm not worried about that', he said. 'There used to be a law against Sunday games, we never took no notice of it, any of us. Not many people knew about it, only people like the Lord's Day Observance Society. But I've got it now, the law was changed about the time the Council started giving permission for the regular club matches over there. This gentleman's mistaken about that. But ball games are not allowed on this field at any time, nothing to do with Sundays—never mind what *he* says.'

'What, never?'

'Never. So now he's started this, I've got to do something about it.'

'But we've played football here every Sunday for years', protested Mr. Prone.

'I dare say', said the keeper. 'Perhaps you've never read the by-laws

—they're on the notice board over there by the entrance gates: no ball games on this field at any time.'

'But why?'

'Well, it's to protect old people and young children, and people who just want a quiet place to walk and sit. That's the idea, I believe. So perhaps if you will just give me your name and address?'

'Why, I never heard anything so daft. My name's Percival Prone, 84 Spenser Road; I'm the newsagent at the corner shop there, Spenser Park General Stores.'

'Ah yes, I know, Mr. Prone.'

The keeper wrote on a tear-off pad and handed a small piece of paper to the man in the long overcoat, who grabbed it.

'Thank you', said the man. '*Now* we'll see who is right about Sunday football. You will be hearing more about this, and so will the Council. You may be interested to know', he added over his shoulder as he moved away, 'that I'm applying for process against four football clubs that were playing over there this morning, and against the Council for allowing them to do it.'

They all watched him walk away, newly bonded to each other by a common distaste.

'He's bonkers', said the park-keeper. 'He's been around here for years, we all know him. You won't hear any more about the Sunday football.' (And they never did.) 'That was changed in 1969. But now this has happened I'm bound to do something about you playing a ball-game on this field. You might get a letter of warning. I hope it won't be anything more.'

It was, in fact, rather less. Mr. Prone had heard no more about it at the time when this account was being compiled. The man in the long overcoat duly learned, no doubt, that the Sunday Observance Act of 1625 had indeed been repealed and that emancipated footballers, cricketers, golfers, tennis and croquet players could now travel outside their parishes on Sundays in order to play. But Prone and son could no longer kick a ball in the field they had used for so long; and at weekends, the only time when they were free to do any kicking in the field where it *was* allowed, every available space was occupied by organized and brightly coloured football teams.

The man in the long overcoat belonged to a past era, the days of the 'common informer'. Common informers were at one time greatly encouraged by the Sunday Observance Acts, which rewarded them with half the penalties imposed by the courts upon their victims. So far as Sunday Observance is concerned, they were abolished in 1951,[1] an

[1] Common Informers Act 1951.

unlamented lot. But it remains a danger for such as Mr. Prone that in any case where a breach of the law is not an *individual* grievance,[1] but is a matter of public policy and 'public morals', then anyone has a general power to inform against him, or bring a private prosecution—or even sue for the penalties as a kind of reward for his representative citizen-ship—unless an Act of Parliament creating the offence says otherwise. There are such men.

Thus when Mr. Prone and son got back to the shop that Sunday evening they realized that the Sabbatarian in the long overcoat and cloth cap, their new Spenser Park acquaintance, was such a man. On leaving the park he had preceded them along Spenser Road and was in the shop when they got home. He was holding a glacial conversation with Mrs. Prone, and in his hands were two or three glossy magazines of the kind which, month by month, portray photographically the most up-to-date economies in the clothing of young women. He looked sadly at Mr. Prone as they came in.

'You!' said Mr. Prone. 'What do *you* want?'

Mr. Prone had had great difficulty about girlie magazines, or what at that time was being called 'soft porn'. He had none about 'hard porn', of which he had his own definition and which he would not allow in his shop. Throughout the fifties and sixties, the law about 'obscene publica-tions' had sustained a nationwide war in which many of the reticences and privacies he had known in his boyhood had been in full retreat. If he could have safely followed his own inclination, he would probably not have sold, and he certainly would not have displayed, any magazine likely to give offence to any minority of his customers. He told himself there was some kind of public responsibility involved. He even accepted that such publications might be harmful to some people, though he understood that everyone saw the harm in them as happening to some-one else. He knew that the law disapproved of publications having any 'tendency to deprave and corrupt' those who were depravable and cor-ruptible. Most of all he believed (though his wife did not) that if his customers couldn't buy their soft porn from him, they would go and buy it in other shops and, once in those shops, buy other things which he really did want to sell.

'I think that's nonsense', Mrs. Prone would say, for she disapproved of the girlie books more strongly than he. (Actually he rather liked them but, for reasons of dignity, kept what it has been fashionable to call a low profile.) 'I think men like to buy those books in shops where no one knows them. Who do you know that comes in here regular, that buys that kind of thing here?'

[1] *R. v. Hicks* (1855), 19 J.P. 515.

Even if he had known, Mr. Prone wouldn't have told her.

'What do *you* want?' he said to the man in the long overcoat, not using the voice he reserved for customers.

The man displayed his purchases. 'I think these are indecent', he said.

'Oh, you do, do you? Let me tell you, everything in this shop, every book and magazine, has been cleared by the police.'

'Indeed?'

'Indeed yes. They came in here months ago, because someone complained, I don't know who put 'em up to it. Someone like you, I suppose. They took a lot of books away, and a week later they brought them all back, every one, and said there would be "no action". That's what they said. So if you go to the police with anything of what I'm selling you'll be wasting your time, mate.'

'Did I say anything about going to the police? I propose to handle this matter myself. I have little confidence in the police. I shall make an application tomorrow morning, in the magistrates' court, for a summons against you under the Indecent Advertisements Act 1889. I shall be acting as a private prosecutor, not a police informer.'

'Indecent advertisement?' said Mr. Prone incredulously. 'What advertisement? What the devil are you talking about? I've never advertised those books. They don't even supply contents bills. D'you mean you've found indecent advertisements *inside* them?'

'The magazines themselves are indecent. The Act deals with many things besides advertisements. It prohibits the exhibition to public view in the window of a shop of a picture or printed matter which is indecent. I shall keep these three magazines as evidence. Good morning.'

And the ping of the shop doorbell as he went out had never sounded so nasty: menacing, official, and final.

It was time to ring up Mr. Parrott the solicitor. 'I shall ring up Mr. Parrott', said Mr. Prone.

'Not on a Sunday evening! There's nothing he can do tonight!'

'He might be able to set my mind at rest, that's what I want. I've been told by the police those books are all right, but there's so many different laws about it, you never know. This bloke seems to have got hold of a new one, indecent advertisements. Well I mean, what's an advertisement?'

'Let's look in the dictionary, Dad', said James. '. . . Advertisement. Here it is. "Public announcement, especially in a public print or by poster or other display".'

'Well,' said Mrs. Prone, 'no one would call one of those magazines a public announcement.'

'I'll get Mr. Parrott to look at the Act', said her worried husband. 'Not much good going by dictionaries.'

Mr. Parrott received the news with the professional fortitude that enables the lawyer to endure so impassively the misfortunes of his clients. But he made no complaint about its being Sunday evening; he would ring back after dinner. Meanwhile, though calm and patient, he was professionally cautious about making any reassuring noises. Mr. Prone did not enjoy his tea. There had never been such a day. How could so many misfortunes assail one man in the course of a few hours? Thank God it was over ... but of course, though this was mercifully unknown to the Prones, it was merely the beginning of The Week.

Mr. Parrott rang.

'I think this may be difficult', he said. 'This man is talking about the Indecent Advertisements Act of 1889. It seems to be very little used, in fact very little known, obsolescent. It's much wider than the Obscene Publications Acts. I'll read you the relevant passage, leaving out the bits that apply only to printed notices and billboards and things. Perhaps you'd like to jot it down and study it at your leisure—I'll read slowly. It's quite short:

Whoever exhibits to any inhabitant, or to any person being in or passing along any street, public highway, or footpath—

Well, you see, that would apply to magazines in your shop window or on the stall outside, but the next bit comes even closer to you—

or exhibits to public view in the window of any house or shop, any picture or printed or written matter which is of an indecent or obscene nature, is liable to a fine of £20 or one month's imprisonment.'

Mr. Prone looked at what he had written, and was conscious of a growing distaste for what he saw.

'But why is it called an Indecent *Advertisements* Act,' he protested, 'if it deals with *any* picture in a shop window?'

'I think there's no doubt it was intended to stop quack advertisements about cures for venereal diseases. There was a lot of that in Victorian times. In fact there's a long section in the Act about nervous debility and complaints arising from sexual intercourse. It says advertisements about those are indecent under this Act if they are posted up on walls or buildings so that the public can see them, but not if they are put up by a local authority. Still, that's not the *only* way a thing can be indecent, you see; it's only one of several ways. Another way, as I said—you've got it written down there—is when it's a picture exhibited to public view in a shop window; and so far as I can see, that's whether it's about venereal disease or not. That's my opinion at the moment. Naught for your comfort, I'm afraid.'

'Oh but look, I've got police clearance for these things, they say they're *not* obscene.'

'There are three things you've got to be clear about. One is that the police have no authority to give "clearance" for anything; the second is that even when you thought they were doing so, they were "clearing" only the particular numbers they had looked at, that week's or that month's issue; and the third is that this Act prohibits anything indecent as well as anything obscene.'

'What's the difference then?'

'Well, a picture can be indecent without being obscene, and that's much easier for the prosecution to prove. To be obscene it must have "a tendency to deprave and corrupt", and I don't think anyone today says these girlie magazines could do that to anyone. But they're hardly decent, are they?'

'You think this man can prosecute me, don't you?'

'I'm sure he can, yes. The prosecution might fail, of course. We should have to do our best. At the moment we can't do anything. Just wait. Let me know if you hear any more about it. Goodbye.'

Mr. Prone took just a little comfort from the phrase 'if you hear any more about it'. But at the close of this long and eventful Sunday he got into bed full of resentment, injury, and misgiving.

'That man means business', said his wife reflectively, and he had a momentary and uncharacteristic longing to press a pillow over her face. 'Perhaps he'll find that only the police can take us to court. They wouldn't do it, not on those silly magazines. Come to that, I believe I read somewhere that a private person can't do it any more, some change in the law. It was after that trial you was interested in, *No Exit to Brooklands*.'

'*Last Exit to Brooklyn*', said Mr. Prone testily, for he was very tired. 'But Mr. Parrott says that wasn't a prosecution, not the first time it came on; that was a special kind of trial with no one in the dock. It was a summons to get the book destroyed, there couldn't have been anyone punished. It was an MP did it,[1] and he won the case and *that* book-seller's copies were destroyed, but the publishers took no notice and went on publishing it. And so then the police took it up, or the Attorney-General or something. And they lost, didn't they? But that was because they were trying to prove the book was obscene, not just indecent.'

'Well, is that what this man is trying to do to us?' said Mrs. Prone sleepily. 'I mean just get those books destroyed?'

'No no, he's talking about a prosecution, Indecent Advertisements Act, I *told* you. That other business was stopped after the *Last Exit* case, that's what you're thinking of, private people applying for "destruction orders". The police can still do it. But this is something quite new. Mr. Parrott says you never hear of this kind of prosecution anywhere.'

'Well, we seem to be hearing about it now. You'd better try and get some sleep, we both had.'

The sleep they got was short and fitful.

[1] Sir Cyril Black, Conservative member for Wimbledon, 1950–70.

Monday

FOR most of us, an alarm clock is at its least likeable on a Monday morning. The distaste with which it is switched off turns to anger as the mind slowly grasps that this is Monday; and the temptation to roll over and cover the head can be dispelled only by yielding to it. Mr. Prone was not like this. Monday, for him, was but little different from Sunday because, although he half-admitted a feeling of satisfaction that his son should occasionally go to the Methodist church on a Sunday, his own attitude to it had become occupationally secular.

A Christian is a man who feels
Repentance on a Sunday

For what he did on Saturday
And means to do on Monday.[1]

As it happened, this Monday began deceptively well. At eight o'clock
Mr. Prone telephoned to the police station to explain to someone in
higher authority why the words PERCIVAL PRONE, LICENSED TO SELL
TOBACCO were no longer painted in one-inch white letters over his
shop doorway. Having explained all this once or twice, he found himself talking to a seemingly knowledgeable station sergeant.

'That's all right,' said the station sergeant, 'you don't need them any
more.'

'Don't *need* them?'

'Not since about 1963, I should think it was. There was a Finance Act
that did away with tobacco licences for shopkeepers. So if you haven't
got a licence, can't get one I mean, well you can hardly tell the world
you're licensed to sell tobacco, can you?'

'But half a minute. Most of the tobacconists round here have got it
painted up, and the Rose and Crown across the road. And the Italian
caff at No. 91—they've just been repainted and had the words done
again.'

'I know, a lot of them do it. Kind of habit. We can't stop them, can
we? Does no harm anyway.'

'But this is all wrong. *Somebody* ought to tell us about a change in the
law like that?'

'Look, come off it Mr. Prone, you must know you're no longer buying
an annual tobacco licence. I haven't heard anything yet from P.C. Flynn,
but it sounds as though he's as muddled as you are. Forget it.'

Mr. Prone hoped, vainly as it turned out, that P.C. Flynn might be
equally muddled about shop blinds, the employment of children, and
highway obstruction. He didn't know, yet, that P.C. Flynn was frighten-
ingly well informed about all these things, and was one of those mercifully rare policemen (every police force endures one) whose duty is their
hobby and obsession, whose favourite light reading is *Moriarty's Police
Law* and to whom *Stone's Justices' Manual* is more gripping than science
fiction. But he had hardly put the telephone down when the retail sale
of tobacco presented him with quite another problem. It was introduced
by Mrs. Prendergast, a long-established customer whose loquacity
made her goodwill as important as her custom. She had just come in and
was talking to his wife.

'I'm sorry I don't like to complain,' Mrs Prendergast was saying, in

[1] Thomas Russell Ybarra, *The Christian* (c. 1905).

the breathless manner commonly found among those who feel at home complaining, 'but you've been selling cigarettes to my Dorothy again she's not fourteen I won't have it I can't always stop her smoking but I can have you stopped selling her cigarettes and if you do it again I shall have to tell the police.' At which point it became necessary for her to breathe.

Mr. Prone couldn't remember Dorothy. 'Does she *look* sixteen?' he asked nervously.

'She hardly looks twelve.'

He swallowed. 'I don't know whether she's bought cigarettes here or not, but if she has and you tell the police' (he braced himself) 'it will mean trouble for her too, won't it?'

'Oh no it won't. That's the way my husband was talking until we inquired about it she doesn't do anything wrong by buying cigarettes *or* smoking them it's up to you not to sell them to children under sixteen and the fine is £25.'

'If she comes in here for cigarettes, how am I to know they're not for you or your husband?'

'Makes no difference we're not smokers anyway but it makes no difference you mustn't sell cigarettes to children under sixteen whoever they're for I'm very sorry,' said Mrs. Prendergast again, 'but my husband says we really must do something about it if it happens again and so did Constable Flynn and he said to come and tell you.'

Mr. Prone started. She was just leaving and he hurried round to stand between her and the door. 'Did you say *Flynn?*' he almost shouted.

'Constable Flynn will be seeing you about your dog,' said Mrs. Prendergast, 'and it coming round and pushing open our chicken house.' Upon which disturbing *non sequitur* she left, tight-lipped but still breathless.

By common consent, the Prones dismissed her. It was time to open the morning letters, for which purpose Mr. Prone withdrew to the parlour. Invoices, circulars, *The Bookseller*, catalogues. . . . What's this?

YOU ARE SUMMONED to attend at the Central Criminal Court, Old Bailey, London, E.C.4, on a date between 1st and 31st December 1976 as directed by the court, to serve as a juror and to remain in attendance at the court from day to day until you are discharged.

'Hey, Martha!'

Mrs. Prone's head came round the edge of the parlour door.

'They want me on a jury. Me! I've never seen one of these before.

How did they get my name? Why me anyway? December? I can't possibly go then, coming up to Christmas, it's ridiculous.'

'Well, I think you just write and say can it be some other time, you're a busy newsagent and it's the one time of year and all like that. Better do it now in case you go and forget.'

The shop-door bell rang, and they both returned to the shop. A fresh-faced young man had come in carrying a small suitcase.

'A very good morning, sir. Would you be interested in some type-writer ribbons, perfect condition, original packings, very cheap?'

'No', said Mr. Prone.

'These are an unusual bargain, unrepeatable, they usually sell at 65 each and I can let you have them at 35.'

'Why?' It was Mrs. Prone's turn.

'Bankrupt stock, and there's plenty more where they came from.'

Mrs. Prone now took an interest. 'Have you got a what's it, a clearance docket,' she asked, 'or something to show where you are getting them from?'

'Certainly madam. Zenith Office Supplies, there you are, invoiced to me, I'm James Croft.'

The Prones examined a grubby document which bore the words Zenith Office Supplies by virtue of a rubber stamp.

'This doesn't say *what* you are', said Mrs. Prone.

'And why should it? I'm a dealer in commercial requisites. Here's my card—oh, I haven't one left, never mind, I can see you're not really interested—'

'Half a moment,' said Mr. Prone, 'don't go dashing off like that. Twenty-five pence each, you said?'

'Thirty-five. How many would you want? I can let you have a gross, my van's outside.'

So Mr. Prone, having carefully counted 144 typewriter ribbons, opened a till not yet depleted by a Monday visit to the Midland Bank, and paid out £50.40 in cash. Neither he nor his wife nor the young man seemed to think the occasion merited the use of a cheque book. In deciding that it did not, Mr. Prone was taking a step which (as will emerge) indicated an attitude of mind which would add to the complications of a crowded week. It would also be of interest to the police. But the fresh-faced dealer in office supplies and commercial requisites, on his way out, was holding the shop door open for Mr. Whiffen, who had the radio and television shop next door and was just coming in.

'I've got a jury summons,' said Mr. Whiffen, 'for December of all times.'

'So have I, that's funny', said Mr. Prone.

Mr. Whiffen saw nothing funny about it. Neither, he said, did Lucas, the chemist along the road, who had also got one. 'They're out to kill the whole Christmas trade stone dead', said Mr. Whiffen.

'Chemists', Mrs. Prone said, 'are exempt from going on juries. Mr. Lucas will be all right.'

'Why should chemists be exempt?' asked Mr. Prone.

'Public need, I suppose', his wife told him. 'Not enough chemists to spare for juries.'

'Well, why send him a jury summons then, I mean if they know he's a chemist? It's wasting everyone's time.'

'They don't know he's a chemist, silly. Not till he tells them. Why should they? They *could* find out before they wrote but they haven't got the time. It's up to him, he'll look on the back of the jury summons and see about chemists not being wanted. Here, give it me again, I'll show you.'

Mr. Whiffen thought all shopkeepers should be exempt, anyway near Christmas. Plenty of people *wanted* to go on juries, idle people, retired, old maids, kids of eighteen—

'Good gracious', said Mrs. Prone. 'Percy, are you still a Special Constable?'

'Eh? No. I don't know. Yes, I suppose I am. I never go these days, I never hear from them. What are you talking about?'

'It says here Special Constables are "persons ineligible for jury service", that's what. I think you're *still* a Special Constable, you'd better find out. Then you can write and tell these jury people and that'll be the end of it.'

Mr. Whiffen could think of nothing suitable to say, sniffed, and picked up one of the recently arrived typewriter ribbons. 'Fifty pee?' he said. 'I'll have one of those.' Then he went back to his shop. Mr. Prone was beginning to think it might be a good idea not to inquire too closely into his membership of the Special Constabulary. Suppose he was no longer regarded as a member, because he'd stopped turning out for occasional duties? Still, he'd got his warrant card somewhere, perhaps in one of the dressing-table drawers, and his truncheon was still somewhere in the garage. He picked up the jury summons again. It bore the telephone number of the 'Jury Summoning Officer'.

'I could find out from there,' he said, 'if they'd tell me on the 'phone.'

'Tell you what?'

'If they've got me down as a Special Constable.'

She looked at him with her head on one side. 'How many ways are there', she said, 'of telling you *they* don't know anything but your name and address and that you've got a vote? That's all they know.' She picked up the jury summons again. 'Why,' she said almost at once, 'I never noticed this—you can't serve on a jury if you've been a Special Constable "at any time within the last ten years". You were certainly out on duty that night the Beatles came, and that was 1967, when I had my gallstones. That settles it, then. You don't have to go. All you do, you just write and tell them.'

There followed what is sometimes called a pregnant pause.

'I wouldn't mind going all that much really,' Mr. Prone faltered, 'if only it wasn't Christmas. They might give me a postponement, say till January or February?'

The backs of Mrs. Prone's hands rose gradually to her hips and tried vainly to find lodgement there. 'Do you want to serve on this jury or don't you? Do you want to be a Special Constable or don't you? If you *are* one, you can't be a juror until ten years after you've stopped being one.'

'Well, I don't need to *tell* anyone. Just say nothing about it. Just say will they have me when Christmas is over.'

'And when Christmas is over you're still just as much a Special Constable as ever, and you propose to go and serve on a jury without telling them. And do you know what happens when they find out?'

'They won't find out.'

'They'll find out because that man Whiffen will tell them, out of jealousy because he won't get excused himself. That's what he will do. And the fine is £400.'

'WHAT?'

'Four hundred pounds—look. Which would just nicely take care of our Christmas profits, wouldn't it?'

'We must think about it. I must get some advice.'

It was time for Mr. Prone to go to the bank. He counted the till cash, got Mrs. Prone to check it, put it in a blue duffel bag, made out his paying-in slip, and went to get the car out.

'I won't be long', he called to his wife, and almost certainly believed what he was saying.

As befitted a Monday morning, a steady drizzle was falling. As Mr. Prone, driving in the offside lane, approached the first set of traffic lights he found it necessary to switch on his windscreen wipers. They did not respond. By the time the lights had changed his windscreen was completely opaque, and all he could do was inch forward in the hope of being able, without mishap, to draw into the near side and see what was wrong. His first timid effort to do this evoked a full-throated and ear-splitting chorus from the impatient motorists behind him. He decided to stop, get out, and (by waving his arms about) convey to these angry drivers that he was in some kind of trouble and that they must be patient and understanding. Thus also he would be able to assess the chances, even perhaps increase them, of pulling in to the near side without a collision. He found that his waving arms merely served as a stimulus, a kind of conductor's beat, to the hymn of hate with which motorists, the world over, will serenade their brothers in misfortune. And having allowed two of them to pass him on the near side, he proceeded to prevent a third by the simple expedient of opening his nearside door and leaving it open; a ruse which added appreciably to the din. Then he drew up to the kerb, got out again, and found himself face to face with a traffic warden. The traffic warden was large, plain, middle-aged, and —in the most forbidding sense of the term—female.

'You very near knocked me over with that door', she said crossly, and already she had a pencil in her hand.

Mr. Prone said he was sorry.

'Where's your tax disc?'

Now he always kept his tax disc on the 'quarter light' by the nearside door, and this he proceeded to point out with some show of injured pride. Moreover it was not an out-of-date one and he felt, in relation to it, the permissibly self-righteous contentment we all feel when our tax discs are not out of date.

'That ought to be on your windscreen', said the traffic warden. 'Near side lower corner', she recited.

'Oh, I've seen lots of these on doors,' Mr. Prone protested, 'specially on big lorries with the windscreen high up. I put it there so it's easy for people like you to read.'

She was not touched. 'All right on a lorry,' she said (she was writing) 'but not for you. What's the matter with the car anyway? What's the idea of holding everyone up at a place like this?'

Mr. Prone was on the point of telling the story of the windscreen wipers when a police car pulled up close to him and a constable got out. He was soon explaining to Mr. Prone that he had committed an offence in not maintaining his windscreen wipers 'in good and efficient working order'.[1] Then he opened the bonnet and examined its contents (always a mystery to Mr. Prone) with the air of expertness which, usually comforting in a roadside mechanic, is sinister and threatening in a policeman.

'You've got no fluid in that windscreen washer, have you?' he said.

'Washer?' Mr. Prone dismally ran his eye along the constable's fore-

[1] Motor Vehicles (Construction and Use), Regulations 1973, Reg. 95.

finger towards an empty plastic container which, he supposed, must be where the windscreen washer kept its water. 'I suppose not', he said. 'I don't know, really. But that's got nothing to do with the wipers not working?'

'Nothing at all', said the policeman. 'It's just another instance of "failing to maintain". Another offence, you see?[1] You must have windscreen wipers that are *capable* of clearing the windscreen, and they can't be capable of clearing one that's caked with mud, can they? That's why you must have fluid in the washer tank. Always keep *some* in there, doesn't matter how little.'

Mr. Prone thanked him, resolving that in future he would keep a lot in; but felt that small progress was being made in the matter of the windscreen wipers. He was also getting rain down his neck. Suddenly he felt his face reddening as the constable asked to see the Ministry of Transport certificate declaring, as required by law,[2] that his elderly car was fit to be among other cars upon the road. This declaration was an annual act of faith by Spenser Motors Ltd., who maintained the vehicle for him; but he happened to know that the 'recorded mileage' on it was understated by about 20,000 miles. The mistake was not his and he had no idea how it had arisen, but he knew it was wrong and he had never done anything about it. Worse was to come.

'Driving licence please?'

'Would you like', said Mr. Prone, who was getting wetter and wetter, 'to get inside the car, where we can do all this in the dry?'

The policeman got in. 'Might as well drive round that corner and stop there', he said. 'Out of the way a bit.'

Mr. Prone drove round the next corner, and noticed that the police car followed. As he searched for his driving licence and insurance certificate, the eyes of the policeman sitting next to him were scanning the interior of the Prone family car. They came to rest upon a duffel bag on the back seat, whose innocent appearance was slightly tarnished by the fact that you could just see, inside it, a linen bag bearing the words MIDLAND BANK and almost certainly containing money.

'What's in there?' said the policeman, patting it, and for once a prompt, simple, and clearly unrehearsed answer was forthcoming.

'A hundred and seventy pounds', Mr. Prone said. 'It's my shop takings since Saturday and I'm taking it to the bank.'

'Ah', said the policeman. 'Ah.' It was inadequate, and yet it sounded like an acquittal on one count, at least. 'This driving licence', he went on, 'expired five weeks ago.'

[1] Ibid., Regs. 26 and 25(2).
[2] Road Traffic Act 1972, section 43.

Mr. Prone was as staggered as we all are when this is revealed to us. While he was still formulating a suitable reply, the policeman struck again. 'And I see you haven't signed it, either.'

'SIGNED it?' Once again Mr. Prone's innocence was genuine. The policeman pointed to the printed words on the licence: Usual Signature of Licence Holder in Ink.[1]

'Oh dear', said Mr. Prone uncertainly. 'Oh dear. So that's another crime, is it?'

'Would be if it was a valid licence. But this isn't a licence at all, you see. An out-of-date one doesn't licence you to do anything. So *your* offence is driving without a licence. So then what makes it worse is that you're not insured either.'

'Oh yes I am insured, officer. Wait a minute, here's my insurance certificate.'

'I'd better see it, yes, but it doesn't have any effect while you're un-licensed. Driving while uninsured, I'm afraid that's rather serious. Three months or £50. . . . Hey! Put that hand-brake on quick, we're moving.'

'I didn't notice, I'm sorry, all these little hills are steeper than you think. There! I've turned the wheels in.'

'Why?'

'Why what? Don't you always turn the wheels to the kerb when you park on a hill?'

There ensued a very short but powerful silence.

'I think you'd better let me sit there a minute.'

'Oh no, we can—'

'Come on, hop out, you'd better come in the passenger's seat and we'll see what else is wrong.'

Reluctantly Mr. Prone changed places with the constable, who straightened up the front wheels and found that the hand-brake didn't hold. The policeman's next words were spoken into his walkie-talkie, and their burden was that Mr. Prone's car was to be towed to the police station for further examination. Very flustered, Mr. Prone suddenly remembered the bank and his bag of money.

'I *must* get this money paid in', he said. 'Please—the bank's only 100 yards up the road there.'

The policeman, absorbed for the moment in pulling up the floor-covering in his eagerness to make new discoveries, didn't look up. 'O.K.,' he said, 'no reason why you shouldn't do that. You nip along

---

[1] Motor Vehicles (Driving Licences) Regulations 1971, Regulation 9: 'Every person to whom a licence is granted shall forthwith sign it in ink with his usual signature.'

and do that. Get back as quick as you can.' And he failed to notice that, once Mr. Prone was out of the car with his bag clutched tightly in both arms, he went off at a rather frantic-looking sprint.

It was noticed, however, by the second policeman, waiting and watching all this time in the patrol car behind. He was in no doubt that Mr. Prone was running away. He leapt from the patrol car and raced after the vanishing little figure with the bag.

Now in London a sprinting policeman and a distant fugitive provide a cameo that never fails to show up the shifting metropolitan public in its three great divisions. There are those who run into shop doorways to get out of trouble and keep out until it has gone away. There are those who stand tip-toe on the kerbstone to watch the fun, without any desire to participate. And there are those, a tiny handful, who join in the chase, knock people over, and often get their hands on the fugitive before the policeman can. It was in the nature of things that Mr. Prone, on this eventful Monday morning, should attract the attention of the third faction. Two of them grabbed him at the same time and he, convinced that this was a particularly audacious attempt at robbery, clutched his bag even more tightly with both arms and began kicking out wildly at his assailants' shins. He made a number of connections with these; and the owner of one shin, letting go of Mr. Prone with a howl, hopped around nursing his leg until he fell to the ground exhausted.

'Help!' screamed Mr. Prone, comfortably drowning the noise of the man with the shin. 'Police!' he added; and his prayer was answered in the person of the constable from the patrol car, who grabbed him. 'Where are you off to with that bag?' demanded this new constable. 'Why did you scramble out of that car with it and run?'

'Oh for God's sake,' said the desperate Mr. Prone, 'it's my money, I'm taking it to the Midland Bank there.'

'You are? O.K., let's go. We'll go there together. If they say you're all right, well that's all right, isn't it? Come on.'

And the party set off in the pouring rain for the Midland Bank, Mr. Prone and his bag of money in the centre, the policeman and an escort of public-spirited citizens ranged around him. As they entered the bank a distant clock was striking half-past twelve. At intervals along the bank counter were positions for five cashiers, four of them unoccupied and exhibiting laconic little notices saying TILL CLOSED. The fifth was occupied by a tense young lady whose little notice said MISS D. WENT-WORTH. She was trying to dispose of a long and self-replenishing queue of bank customers, a process which had been held up for some time by the man at the head of the queue, who was wearing a blue boiler-suit and rubber shoes. He had presented a 'bearer' cheque which Miss D.

Wentworth was gazing at suspiciously. They all looked up in alarm as the Prone procession entered.

'Do you know this man miss?' said the policeman, pushing forward Mr. Prone, and she looked at him carefully.

'No,' she said, truthfully (for she was new at the branch), 'I've never seen him.'

'Bit awkward for you, isn't it?' said the policeman to Mr. Prone.

'Why that's Mr. Prone', said the man in the blue boiler-suit. 'Why, 'ullo Percy, what's up then, mate?'

Mr. Prone, who might ordinarily have blessed the presence of someone who knew him, on this occasion was none too pleased. He was just about to say why, when the man held up both his hands and said 'all right, all right, you just explain all this to the policeman', and walked quickly out of the bank. For the moment all eyes followed him, but he was soon forgotten as Mr. Prone set about satisfying the police and the cashier, by producing his Midland Bank paying-in book and giving the number of his account, that he was a righteous citizen seeking merely to pay in his own money. This having been done without further difficulty, there arose the question of the man in the boiler-suit and his parting suggestion that Mr. Prone could explain all.

'Explain all what?' said the constable.

'I have absolutely no idea what he was talking about', Mr. Prone said, unwittingly using the precise formula that all conspirators use when the police first catch up with them.

'But you know him, do you? He seemed to know you?'

'He's an odd-job man, he's done a few things for me at the shop.'

And this is the point at which to reveal that the man in the boiler-suit, who had overheard the Prones' conversation about typewriter ribbons, had seen at once that Mr. Prone's indiscretion might be turned to good advantage.

'Did he leave his cheque behind?' asked the policeman, rather belatedly, and Miss D. Wentworth held it up. It was for £100, it was payable to 'Bearer', and it bore the name Percival Prone, once in printed letters and, below that, once in a handwriting that was vaguely similar (Mr. Prone angrily noted) both to his own signature and to the handwriting of the word 'Bearer'. Then he began to explain.

'His name's Pilgrim. I only know him as Pilgrim, I don't know where he comes from.'

And Pilgrim, he said, being called in that very morning to do something about the shop-blind, had come across Mr. Prone's cheque-book lying forgotten and uncared for. Only the scepticism of Miss Wentworth had prevented him from lightening the Prone current account by

£100. For the second time Mr. Prone then heard one end of a police walkie-talkie conversation; this time giving a brief description of the departed Pilgrim, followed by the story of the stolen cheque-book and the forged cheque.

Their return to Mr. Prone's car happened to coincide with the arrival of a police tender, equipped for towing away cars that the police deem eligible for towing away. The waiting policeman seemed to think Mr. Prone's reappearance was long overdue, but the latter's excited narrative filled in the time until they all reached the police-station yard. And it was here that Mr. Prone was to learn the worst.

'You'll have to leave it with us for the time being', said one of the policemen. 'We must go over it.' He was dismayed. What on earth might they not find wrong with it now?

'But how do I get home?'

'Bus, I suppose. Or walk? But before you start, the CID want a word with you, I believe. Perhaps you'll step this way a moment?'

CID? What was all this? The constable shepherded him towards a door marked 'CID Sergeants', on the other side of which he was greeted by a young man who seemed unexpectedly (and, truth to tell, disturbingly) amiable. 'Sit down, Mr. Prone,' he said, 'you and I have some talking to do.'

'What? I've got no talking to do. I want to get back to my shop, my wife's got no help there till next week.'

'Well yes, *very* shortly. But first of all—'

'Look here, am I being detained or something?'

There was a very long pause.

'Why should you be detained? You haven't done anything we could detain you for, have you? Well, I mean, *have* you?'

'Nothing whatever. Well, there's all that business about the car—'

'Oh no no, not the car. That's all being looked after by the uniform branch. I mean about this, um, typewriter ribbon.'

And in a horrible silence the detective sergeant held up a freshly straightened-out square of tinfoil, upon which there rested an empty typewriter spool.

'Where did *that* come from?' said Mr. Prone unsteadily, with a feeling that he knew the answer.

'Well now, I'll tell you. A Mr. Whiffen came in with it, to say that he bought it in your shop this morning for fifty pence, in the belief that it was a new ribbon. It was all neatly wrapped in this tinfoil, he said. And when he got home and unwrapped it, he found it was only an empty spool.'

'WHAT? Empty? I don't believe it', said Mr. Prone. His immediate past was coming up to hit him. 'A Mr. Whiffen, did you say?'

'A radio and television dealer, 86 Spenser Road. That's near you, isn't it?'

'Next door. What did he say?'

'Just that he bought this in your shop this morning, I suppose it was about a couple of hours ago. And he seemed very angry. He said it was all wrapped in tinfoil to make it look new. And the person who sold it to him was Mrs. Prone, that's your wife, is it sir?'

'Yes it is. Let me look at that ribbon. . . . Why, the blasted rogue!'

'Mr. Whiffen?'

'The bloke who came in this morning and sold me a gross of these things. Sold them as new, bankrupt stock he said.'

'That's what I was wondering. You see, we have a report about the theft of a whole lorry-load of typewriter ribbons.'

'What! Used-up ones? Who the hell would steal old typewriter ribbons no good to anyone?'

'No no, that's the funny part, you see. Someone's been busy collecting up old typewriter spools and wrapping them in tinfoil to look new. Then they sell a gross at a time, to somebody like you, and only the top few in each box are genuine ribbons. They probably flog the genuine ones somewhere else. Got it?'

Mr. Prone had got it. Getting out of his chair, he said, 'I want to telephone my wife.'

'Well, yes, all in good time.'

'No no, I must call her *now*. I've been away a couple of hours, she'll be wondering what the devil has happened. I was only going to the bank, it never takes me more than twenty minutes. Where's the telephone please?'

The sergeant knew from experience that a man in Mr. Prone's predicament, given the use of a telephone, will tell his wife to dispose of the typewriter ribbons as rapidly as possible. The sergeant could even suppose that a good wife, and Mrs. Prone was a good wife, might dispose of them unbidden on the strength of what she knew already. Details such as these called for discussion before Mr. Prone should be encouraged to resume outside contacts. He was told to sit down again.

'Look here, let's have no more nonsense about this. Am I under arrest?'

'No no, nothing of the kind. No need to be dramatic about it.'

'Right, then I can go?'

'Well, not exactly. I mean you couldn't go any distance to speak of. Far as the station door, perhaps.'

'So I *am* under arrest? If you won't let me leave this building, I'm arrested.'

'Let's put it this way, shall we, and now we are speaking very frankly? We want to know how you came by these typewriter ribbons, and how much you paid for them, and who to, and what kind of enquiry you made about their origin, and what you knew about the man you bought them from—that kind of thing. Did he give you an invoice or a receipt? And so on. If your answers make us think this is a case of "dishonest handling", or receiving as the law used to call it, well then we shall make a charge against you. And by that time we shall have arrested you.'

Mr. Prone's mind was working at unwonted speed.

'I see. So I'm not arrested at the moment, and in fact I won't be arrested unless I say something you're half expecting me to say, is that it? Well, I've said all I'm going to say. And now I want to go.'

'It's not exactly like that. Agreed that you're not under arrest at the moment—you're just giving me information. But giving me further information isn't the *only* way of getting yourself arrested. You might do that, in the end, by not saying anything at all.'

'Are you saying I've got to *talk* myself out of being arrested?'

'All dramatic again, you see?' (Sharply) 'How much did you pay for those ribbons?'

Mr. Prone had a sudden thought. Mr. Parrott!

'I'm not saying any more, I'm not answering any more questions,' he said, 'until my solicitor is here. Mr. Stephen Parrott, he's on the 'phone, Parrott and Parrott, 228 Everton Road. I want to 'phone him please.'

The door suddenly opened.

'Mrs. Prone is here, sergeant', said the bearded young face that appeared round the edge of it.

'Ah, good. Come in will you, and stay with Mr. Prone? I'll go and see her.'

And the detective sergeant went out. Mr. Prone glared at his new guardian with alarm and distaste.

'What was that you said? Where is she? What's my wife doing here?'

'She's helping us with our enquiries about some stolen typewriter ribbons.'

'Good God, where is the end of all this? Have you arrested *her* now?'

'No no, she came along with us, mostly to find out where *you* were. But she seems to know quite a lot about the typewriter ribbons, doesn't she?'

'I want my solicitor called at once.'

The young detective nodded, sat down, folded his arms, and began whistling very quietly as he looked vacantly into the middle distance.

Communication remained on this level for another five minutes: and then the telephone rang. 'Sergeant Dean's office?' said the constable into it. 'Right, sergeant, we'll be along.'

'Time to come and see your wife', he said to Mr. Prone. And they found her looking uncharacteristically flustered in another interview room, with Detective Sergeant Dean and a young woman in police uniform.

'Percy!' cried Mrs. Prone. 'Are you all right? Goodness, you've given me a scare. This gentleman says we can go, but I didn't know there was any question about being *allowed* to go. What does he mean? I'll tell you what I think, you and I have been swindled, that's what.'

As Mr. Prone stood mutely before his wife, Sergeant Dean spoke for him.

'We think it's unlikely there will be any charge against you or your wife', he said. 'The position is, the cartons of supposed typewriter ribbons have been opened and nearly every one of them is in fact an empty spool. There were only four new ribbons among the lot, and they've been identified as coming from a stolen lorry-load. Your wife was most helpful in unwrapping them with us this morning.'

As sometimes happens when a man is having difficulty in finding the right words, Mr. Prone's jaws were opening and closing silently.

'Charge against *us*?' said Mrs. Prone while this was going on. 'What have *we* done? If there's any charge against anyone, surely it's against that young man who sold the things to us?'

'If we find him,' the sergeant said, 'he will certainly be charged with stealing them. But as to whether you charge him with obtaining money from you by deception, well, h'm, I should think you ought to ask your solicitor about that.'

'Why?'

'It might expose you to some awkward questions in court, you see, even if you got the police to take it up on your account.'

'Such as?'

'Well, such as how you came to be buying typewriter ribbons from a stranger at 35 pence a time, Mrs. Prone. . . . Come on, the patrol car will run you both back home.'

'Who on earth's looking after the shop all this time?' Mr. Prone asked his wife in the back of the police car. 'Jimmy can't be there, it's long past his dinner time?'

'I got Sheila to come in. Well, she may as well start today, her mother says she's dying to leave school anyway. We'll see. What was that man saying about someone at the bank this morning with a forged cheque?'

He told her quickly of his morning's adventures. The two policemen in the front seats listened impassively with the backs of their necks until he came to the point where Pilgrim, the man in the boiler-suit, had walked unhindered from the bank. Then one of them said:

'You didn't seem too anxious to stop him, Mr. Prone? I mean he *was* trying to do you out of £100 with a forged cheque, you knew that?'

'What happens about that now?' Mr. Prone said wearily.

'Oh we're looking for him all right. If you don't want to prefer any charge against him, we shall charge him ourselves, no doubt.'

Mr. Prone wouldn't mind that, he said, so long as he wasn't brought into it. But on this point he had to be quickly disillusioned: if Pilgrim were arrested and brought in, there would be charges of stealing a cheque book, uttering a forged cheque with intent to defraud, forging the cheque, all sorts of things; and Mr. Prone *must* be brought in, as a witness for the prosecution. Then if Pilgrim were defended, his counsel would be quite likely to mention Mr. Prone's purchase of the stolen typewriter ribbons.

'Why?' said Mr. Prone crossly. 'Why?'

'Because Pilgrim was relying on that to keep you quiet. Bit complicated, isn't it? Still, here's your shop. We'll keep in touch, shall we? We'll want you as a witness anyway if we catch the bloke who sold that stuff to you. So long.'

Mr. and Mrs. Prone got out of the car without replying. They were sitting down to a very late cold lunch before they felt able to mention the matter again.

'If we have to give evidence about buying those typewriter things,' said Mrs. Prone, 'we shall be in the soup. They'll want to know why we thought it was all right to pay only 35 pence.'

'Bankrupt stock. I'm not going to worry about that. What we've done is pay £50 for three or four ribbons and more than a hundred empty spools. No one's going to prosecute us for that.'

'I'm not so sure. But anyway think of the disgrace!' said Mrs. Prone. 'The local paper! The neighbours, the family, everybody. Oh I don't know how I'm going to look customers in the face again.'

'I shall look 'em in the face,' said Mr. Prone slowly, speaking with his mouth full, 'because every single one of 'em would have done the same as what we did.'

They had scarcely finished their custard when they heard the voice of P.C. Flynn in the shop again.

'Ah,' said P.C. Flynn as they came out of the parlour together, 'do you know a Mrs. Prendergast?'

'I do,' Mr. Prone said, 'and you can take it from me, nobody here has sold her daughter cigarettes, ever. We don't serve cigarettes to children.'

'I hadn't heard about the cigarettes', P.C. Flynn said gratefully. 'That must be something fresh. Would you like to tell me about it now?'

Mr. Prone indicated that he would not. 'There's nothing to tell', he said. 'She says someone has sold cigarettes to her daughter, but it wasn't here. I can't help you about that.'

'Ah well, I suppose we shall hear some more about it. Meanwhile I was going to ask about your dog. A Labrador, they tell me. Does he happen to be at home?'

'Bruno?' said Mrs. Prone. 'He was here this morning. Why?'

'It's like that, is it? You don't know where he is at any given moment? Wanders about like?'

'And what's wrong with that?' asked Mr. Prone.

'If he's going to run loose,' said P.C. Flynn, 'he's got to do three things. He's got to keep out of mischief, and always look as if he knows where he's going, and always wear a collar with his name and address on. He seems to have let you down in every way.'

The Prones looked at each other in dismay. Jimmy, they both re-called, had a way of taking Bruno's collar off to brush him, and forgetting to put it on again. And Bruno, it had to be admitted, occasionally got out and roamed the streets, sometimes collarless. This did not conceal his identity from such as Mrs. Prendergast, whose love of itinerant dogs was conditioned by the fact that she herself kept chickens on her allotment. Her complaint, it now transpired, was that Bruno, who was too bulky to get inside her chicken house, had pushed open its flimsy chicken-wire door and got his fat body stuck in the opening. In wriggling free, while the chickens watched helplessly from the most distant perches provided, Bruno had considerably distorted the shape of the chicken house, in which Mr. Prendergast had taken a modest do-it-yourself builder's pride. Towards the end of P.C. Flynn's recital of this episode, the shop door opened to admit a customer; and while the door was open, Bruno trotted in too. As he sniffed around P.C. Flynn's boots his long tail was swishing with the happy innocence of one who knows himself to be collarless and yet is unashamed.

Impassively P.C. Flynn wrote something in his little book. 'Quite a number of offences here', he said approvingly. 'First, allowing your dog to be in a highway or place of public resort while not wearing a collar bearing your name and address.[1] I suppose you will be very surprised

[1] Control of Dogs Order 1930.

to know that the maximum penalty for that is a fine of £400.'[1]

'WHAT!' screamed Mr. Prone. 'Four hundred pounds because a dog gets out and goes after some chickens?'

'No. Four hundred pounds because he gets out with no collar on. I was coming to the chickens.'

'I simply don't believe it.'

'I'm only telling you what the law says, Mr. Prone. I daresay it seems a lot. Now about him worrying the chickens, that's a fine of £20; unless he's done it before, in which case it's £50.[2] And then there's the Road Traffic Acts. You mustn't permit your dog to be on a "designated road" without him being held on a lead.[3] This happens to be a designated road, and he seems to spend a lot of time on it, which is very dangerous for everyone. Still, that's only a fine of £20, which is odd, isn't it? I suppose they know what they're doing. Then of course all the time he's on his own in a highway or place of public resort the law regards him as a stray dog,[4] whether he's got a collar on or not.'

'Another £400, perhaps?' suggested Mr. Prone bitterly.

'Well no. He can be seized and taken to the police station, and anyone can do that, not just a policeman. I mean, Mrs. Prendergast could do it, even though she knows he belongs to you. Then you would have to claim him and pay for the cost of looking after him.'

A terrible thought was climbing into the back of Mr. Prone's mind. Suppose he *didn't* claim Bruno from a police station? He had never been passionately fond of Bruno. Bruno was his wife's dog.

'Suppose I didn't claim him?' he asked.

'We would keep him for seven days and then have him put down.'

When P.C. Flynn had gone again, Mrs. Prone looked at her husband searchingly. 'What was the point of *that* inquiry?' she asked him.

He said it was nothing, but it was in fact a symptom of what the law was beginning to do to the life of a once ignorant man. And it was a preoccupied Mr. and Mrs. Prone who then addressed themselves, for the remainder of that Monday afternoon, to what had once seemed the humdrum and honourable occupation of selling corner-shop goods; no longer humdrum because everybody seemed to know what had been going on, and to be full of sympathy and the desire to know more; no longer honourable because every step of the way had come to seem

---

[1] Diseases of Animals Act 1950, sect. 79.
[2] Dogs (Protection of Livestock) Act 1953.
[3] Road Traffic Act 1972, sect. 31.
[4] Dogs Act 1906, sect. 3.

furtive and fraught with danger. The little shop was crowded for the rest
of the day as each customer prolonged his transaction with gossip, com-
miseration, and what he thought about the Laws of England and their
impact on the individual: their impact, that is to say, on the popular
and now (in every sense) exemplary Mr. Prone.

It was on one Monday evening in each month that he went to the
Rotary Club as a member of its Community Service Committee. This
was one of those Mondays, and he was of course without his car, which
was still at the police-station yard and seemed destined for a series of
operations and a prolonged convalescence. It was still raining, he felt dis-
inclined to walk, and he decided to make one of his rare appearances on
a London bus. This one was likely to be more memorable than most
because he happened to be carrying four billiard-cues, each in a metal
case, which he was proposing to present to the Rotary Club Committee
for the use of its recently founded boys' club. Let it be admitted that
this gift was involving him in but a minor sacrifice: the billiard cues had
lain forgotten in the loft for many years, no one quite remembered who
their original owner had been, and sooner or later they would have been
got rid of as a gift to someone.

The nearest bus stop was a couple of hundred yards along the road
towards Spenser Park, and by the time he got there Mr. Prone was
rather wet. By the time the crowded bus got there, nearly fifteen minutes
later, he was not only much wetter; he was angry about the bus service
and its basic operative principle that passengers are to be regarded as a
nuisance. As he got on he saw that there were people standing inside,
and that the conductor was apparently upstairs. Something told him,
perhaps it was the effects of the day's events, that if he joined the standing lower-deck passengers he would be made to get off when the conductor came down. So he went upstairs, to meet the conductor at the top.

'You can't bring them things up here', said the conductor, with only
the briefest of glances at them.

'They're only billiard cues', pleaded Mr. Prone. 'Is there some law
against billiard cues?'

'There's a law against entering or travelling on a bus with a cumbersome article,[1] unless you have the consent of an authorized person.
That's me, and I'm telling you them things are cumbersome and not
allowed on this bus.'

By this time they were back on the conductor's platform and the conductor had rung the bell for the bus to stop. And in Mr. Prone, who
two or three days before would have meekly got off the bus, anger boiled

[1] Public Service Vehicles (Conduct of Drivers Conductors and Passengers)
Regulations 1936, Reg. 10.

over once again, totally ousting discretion. Recklessly he reached up and pressed the button for the bus to continue its journey. Angry too, the conductor reached up and gave his driver, who was just moving off again, the emergency signal which brought the vehicle to a stop with a jerk.

'I want your name and address please', he now told Mr. Prone.

'What for?'

'For giving a signal to the driver to start.[1] You've got no right to do that, and I shall report you to the police.'

'Well,' shouted the exasperated Mr. Prone as he jumped off the bus into the rain, 'you're getting no name and address out of me, I can tell you that. I've had enough of that kind of thing today.'

'What seems to be the trouble then?' said a confident voice behind them, and there (believe it or not) stood a policeman, shining wet, very large, and (Mr. Prone thought) totally and malevolently inopportune.

Gratefully the conductor gave the officer a rapid outline of the billiard-cue episode, and towards the end of it the constable was groping in the recesses of his wet clothing for notebook and pencil. 'Your name and address, sir, please?'

Sullenly and reluctantly Mr. Prone declared and identified himself. There was a considerable delay while the policeman went on to record also the name and number of the complaining conductor, and the various details of the bus itself; in the course of which another bus arrived, a half-empty one. After one moment's hesitation, Mr. Prone dashed to it and got on, unhindered by anyone. The conductor on this one watched indulgently as Mr. Prone laid his billiard cues along the floor at his feet, and the bus was off and away before anyone could attempt to stop it. As he settled in his seat he found himself thinking that, if the law really said 'cumbersome article' and no more, it left too much to the imagination and discretion of any cantankerous bus conductor. What it really said (and it could hardly say less?) was that 'a passenger or intending passenger must not enter or travel in or on a vehicle with loaded firearms, or any dangerous or offensive article or, except with the consent of an authorized person, bring into or on the vehicle any bulky or cumbersome article, or place any such article elsewhere in or on the vehicle than as directed by an authorized person'. This conductor, reflected Mr. Prone, seemed not to mind the four billiard cues in the least. He supposed all conductors conducted differently. Anyway this must surely be the very last, dying kick that the law could direct at him at the end of this incredible day.

It was not.

[1] Ibid., Reg. 9(viii).

Two hours later as he came out of the King's Arms, wherein the Rotary Club held its meetings, and crossed the road to wait for yet another bus, he was approached by yet another policeman. By this time he disapproved of all policemen, approaching or retreating. But he truly hated the sight of an approaching one.

'Excuse me sir', the policeman said in the ingratiating tone which, whatever it might happen to bode, can so often bode no good. 'Have you got ten minutes to spare?'

He had not. For the police, at any rate, he had less than ten seconds to spare. But he supposed he had better find out how the ten minutes would have been employed.

'What for?' he said frostily.

'We want about eight or nine people like you, I mean like you in appearance, to help us with an identity parade. We've got a man in custody on suspicion of armed robbery, and we've got to "put him up" for identification by four witnesses.'

Mr. Prone stared.

'Do I look like an armed robber?' he demanded.

'No, but neither does this chap. Come to that, who does? He's about your height and build and he wears glasses. We wouldn't keep you a minute.'

'You said ten minutes.'

'Well, you know what I mean. It's all very quick really.'

'Suppose,' said Mr. Prone, peering along the wet road to see if a bus was coming, 'suppose one of the witnesses picks *me* out?'

'Well then it's a failure, isn't it? I mean he's wrong, isn't he? We say thank you very much for your help and that's the end of it. '

Mr. Prone was far from satisfied. 'Suppose *all four* of them pick me out?'

'Well, that just won't happen, it never does. And even if it did, that wouldn't necessarily mean we let the suspect go, it only means those four witnesses are not much good. Come on sir, give us a few minutes, just to see justice done.'

Mr. Prone took a few irresolute and reluctant steps with the constable by his side, and realized, having done so, that there was no turning back. 'What about my bus?' he said, his eyes suddenly narrowing; 'how do I get home—I live along the Spenser Road, No. 84.'

'O.K., we'll be able to run you home.'

The police station was not the one that he knew, not the scene of his interrogation that morning and the present home of his unhappy car. Inside it he was soon introduced to a large room (it was a parade room) glaringly illuminated by striplighting, and was asked to stand in a line, side-by-side with seven other men, all of whom were of about his build but not all of whom were wearing glasses. After a few uneasy minutes, during which none of the eight men said anything, an unhelmeted policeman emerged from one of several doors carrying a cardboard box full of spectacles.

'These are all "found property" glasses,' he said to everyone, 'handed in during the past three months. Perhaps you gentlemen without glasses wouldn't mind trying on a pair—it's best to find a pair that doesn't make you squint or look uncomfortable.'

In due course everyone was wearing spectacles, though Mr. Prone was unable to see from where he stood whether everyone looked comfortable in them. One of their number, he supposed, was the suspect, but this was not to be deduced from the way any one of them was treated by the police. Several men he assumed to be detective officers were standing about, until there appeared a brisk-looking senior officer who announced that the time had come for them all to clear out and for the parade to begin. Then from another door the first of the four witnesses was brought in. He was asked to look along the line of men and, if he saw among them the man he had already described to the police, to touch that man on the shoulder. He was also most carefully told not to *assume* that the suspect was actually among them anyway. With hardly a moment's hesitation the witness walked straight up to Mr. Prone and touched him.

'Look, I say,' said Mr. Prone, 'I know nothing about all this, absolutely nothing.'

'That's O.K. sir,' said a police officer, 'don't worry. Next witness please.'

The mistaken witness having been led away through yet another door, a second witness appeared and was given similar instructions. He stood for a moment looking along the line of men, then walked straight to Mr. Prone and touched him.

'That's the man,' he said, 'I'd know him anywhere.'

The jaws of the utterly aghast Mr. Prone began opening and shutting in the way they did when he was trying to say something too poignant for speech. By the time the two remaining witnesses had also picked him out as an armed robber, he had gone very white but his jaws had stopped moving and the gift of speech had been restored to him.

'You're crazy,' he shrieked, 'the whole damn lot of you. Crazy. What do you want with me now? I'm going, I've had enough of this nonsense. . . .'

'I wonder if you'd pipe down for just a moment?' said the senior detective officer soothingly. 'Thank you gentlemen. There are cups of coffee on this table here for anybody who would like one. Perhaps you'll leave your names and addresses with the officer at the other table as you go out?'

There was no reason why they *should* leave their names and addresses if they didn't want to, no law to compel them. And two of them declined to do so, deeming it prudent accordingly to refuse the cup of coffee also; and they left. Conversation broke out among the others around the coffee table.

'They picked out the wrong bloke then?' said one.

'They all picked *me* out', said Mr. Prone angrily, who was nevertheless drinking a cup of police coffee. 'That's what you get for agreeing to help the police.'

'That's what I was thinking', said another man. 'Plus a cup of coffee —I suppose this is all we get?—I should have thought they'd give us a quid or two for our trouble and time.' No one cared, or dared, to remind him that he was a volunteer, however little he might have felt like one; and that volunteers are seldom paid.[1] There was, however, a general feeling of sympathy for Mr. Prone. Was he really saying that he had been recruited from the street, like all the rest of them?

'Well, what do you *think*?' spluttered Mr. Prone, glaring round at them. 'Do you think I'm a bank robber?'

'No no,' said one of them hurriedly, 'but I suppose one of us was. Which one was he? Has he gone?'

'Two blokes have gone,' said another, 'they wouldn't give their names and addresses and they just scarpered. But it couldn't have been either of *them*—the police wouldn't let their suspect go like that. Well, that ought to leave six of us, and there's only five. Where's the other one, then?'

'The other one,' said the detective officer, rejoining them at that moment, 'is the suspect, and he's in another room. Thank you very much for your help gentlemen, and I'll bid you all goodnight.'

The five men took this to mean that it was now time for them to go; and four went. But just as Mr. Prone was leaving, a voice in his ear said, 'Perhaps you could give us a *little* more of your time, sir, just to clear up one or two things?'

'Clear up one or two things?' he said. 'Like what?'

The detective officer coughed. 'We think you might feel more comfortable in your own mind if you could satisfy us where you were at 5.30 yesterday afternoon. You see on Sunday three men broke out of the

---

[1] As to this, the practice of the police varies throughout the country. Staffordshire Police in 1976 began paying their identity parade 'volunteers' £1 each; which may have begun paving the way towards a nation-wide munificence, but it will take a long time.

Midland Bank at Derry Street and were picked up by a blue Vauxhall car; and the four witnesses you have just seen are people who saw them running to the car. They gave us good descriptions of two of the men and we have a man in custody. I must say he resembles you *very* closely, sir.'

'I suppose', said Mr. Prone, 'there's some sort of a difference between resembling me and actually *being* me? Are you trying to tell me now that the bloke you've got in that room is Percival Prone, newsagent and tobacconist, 84 Spenser Road, and that I'm somebody else?'

The detective started. 'Prone?' he said. 'Prone the newsagent? Well, that makes it nice and easy. That's someone we *do* know about. Perhaps you've got some proof of identity in your pocket? Driving licence? I'm sorry I don't happen to know you personally.'

Mr. Prone remembered the expiry date on his driving licence, and had no wish to start *that* inquisition all over again. 'What you *can* do,' he said, 'is telephone my wife. She'll tell you who I am. She'll tell you that at 5.30 yesterday I was in Spenser Park playing football with my son and some other boys; I gave my name and address to a park-keeper there, because there was a complaint from someone about Sunday football.'

And that is what, within a few minutes, a startled and incredulous Mrs. Prone *did* tell them.

'Bank robber!' she said, when the police car had driven away and Mr. Prone at last sat exhausted in the shop parlour. 'Did somebody suppose *you* looked like a *bank* robber?' She suddenly gave way to unrestrained laughter, in which Mr. Prone did not join. 'I never heard anything so ridiculous in all my life. Why, anyone's only got to take one look at you—'

She was overdoing the thing; wifely loyalty and ill-concealed derision, an uncomfortable but not unprecedented mix, were assuming a texture in which the derision was the more easily seen.

'If I got into a bank to do a robbery,' he said, 'I wouldn't come blundering out of it in broad daylight on a Sunday afternoon. And I'll tell you something else. If ever I get asked again by the police to go on one of their identity parades, I shall tell them to go to hell. That's what I shall tell them', said Mr. Prone, and as he said it he summoned up a look of ferocity from which his wife could usefully draw material for fresh thought about her husband as an improbable bank robber.

Tuesday

It was twenty-five past eight and a cold morning. Mrs. Prone, in slacks and a short padded coat, was setting out the papers and magazines on the front stall—in defiance of P.C. Flynn's disapproval of that useful structure. 'Sheila!' she called over her imitation sheepskin shoulder, 'will you just shake the mats out here before you go?'

Hearing which, Mr. Prone protruded his head round the edge of the shop door. 'It's nearly half-past eight', he said. 'She ought to be gone, she says she's had no real breakfast.'

'Is it half-past *already*?' asked his wife, to whom clocks seemed to record a different dimension from the one that ruled her life.

'Oh that's all right', said Sheila as she came out of the shop. 'I'm not going to school today.'

Sheila Best came to help in the shop from seven o'clock until eight-thirty every morning except Sunday. At the time of this episode she was a little over fifteen and a beneficiary, though she regarded herself as a victim, of the law's recent decision that no one was to leave school before the age of sixteen. Her parents strongly disapproved of this law, thought she should be working for her living (and theirs), and turned a blind eye to the truancies by which, it seemed, she was fitting herself for an early adult life. Sheila herself had declined to have anything to do with O-level examinations or even the Certificate of Secondary Education. Or with school, period. But hitherto she had left the Prones promptly at 8.30 every morning and they had supposed she then went to school.

'Not going to school?' said Mr. Prone. 'Is it a holiday then?'

'For me it is. I didn't go yesterday either.'

'Shake the mats for me Sheila, will you?' Mrs. Prone said unconcernedly, and Sheila sauntered back into the shop to get them.

'Look, if she's playing truant from school she can't work here', said the anxious Mr. Prone. 'Not after 8.30 anyway. I've always wanted her to go at eight o'clock, as you know.'

'She likes the extra bit of money. It's all right, forget it. There's thousands of them staying away, this compulsory sixteen business is nonsense—she says at school she spends the whole day doing nothing, absolutely nothing.'

'Well, I don't believe it, see? That's only what she says.'

But he hurried indoors because by this time Sheila was busily banging door mats on the kerbstone and raising clouds of dust which, whatever it might be doing to other people's, began to affect his throat. It must have been part of a universal and, on the whole, malevolent design that P.C. Flynn should just at that moment be passing by, a process which he always seemed glad to interrupt.

'Good morning Mrs. Prone', he said without eliciting any reply. 'I suppose you know what the time is?'

The silence continued.

'What's your name then?' he said to Sheila, who had by this time piled three newly shaken doormats upon each other and was about to carry them indoors.

'Sheila Best, what's yours?' she said cheerfully.

'Address?'

Mrs. Prone now spoke for the first time. 'This address will do,' she said, 'she works here. What do you want with her?'

'How old are you, Sheila?' asked P.C. Flynn.

'She's fifteen', Mrs. Prone said. 'And you'll make her late for school. All right, leave them there Sheila, you'd better be off.'

And Sheila, suddenly filled with a revised intention about school, hurried away.

'Don't you know about beating or shaking doormats in the streets?' resumed P.C. Flynn, with the air of a man reaching the main point on the agenda. 'You can't do that after eight o'clock.' He produced a little book from his inexhaustible pocket. 'Here it is, if you're really interested. These are all things you can't do in the street:

Every person who in any thoroughfare shall beat or shake any carpet rug or mat (except doormats before the hour of eight in the morning)—

and there's a fine of forty shillings.'[1]

Mr. Prone came out as this was being read. 'What's all this?' he said to P.C. Flynn. 'Don't you ever sleep? Have a day off? Fall downstairs and break something?'

'You employ a girl named Sheila Best, and under your wife's instruction she has just been shaking mats in the street, which is against the law.'

'Not doormats', said Mr. Prone, barely able to conceal his triumph—he had come across this before. 'Those are doormats.'

'The exemption for doormats ends at eight o'clock. Carpets and rugs, not allowed at all. Doormats, up to eight o'clock. I shall have to report this matter, you see.'

'Are you really telling me you're going to prosecute a child for shaking a doormat? Why, you'll be absolutely smothering yourself in glory.'

'No, I shall probably proceed against Mrs. Prone—she gave the order. And then there's the question of the girl's employment, on a day when she's required to attend school.'

'Well, you're on a loser there. She comes here from seven in the morning to eight-thirty, that's all.'

'Ah. Normally, you see, you can't employ a registered school pupil before the close of school hours. Actually in this district, by a special local regulation, you *may* employ such a child for not more than one

[1] Metropolitan Police Act 1839, section 60, sub-section 3.

hour before school begins.[1] Seven to eight-thirty is an hour and a half, I'm afraid.'

'Blimey, you'll earn yourself the title of nit-picker of the year, you will.'

P.C. Flynn was armour-plated. 'You will probably hear', he said, 'from the Education Department about Sheila Best. The school will know how often she's been away, without knowing *where* she's been. They will be interested. It looks as though you may be able to help them.'

Mr. Prone glanced at his wife and decided to say nothing. He had sometimes noticed that Sheila's school had more holidays than the one attended by his daughter Susan; but in the company of P.C. Flynn he was proposing to leave unanswered any questions that were not asked as well as any that were. That insatiable officer was meanwhile passing to another topic.

'On Sunday,' he was saying, 'I told you about the Highways Act of 1959 and the obstruction being caused by your news-stand here. You seemed to think you'd got hold of some Common Law right to use it because you haven't actually been prosecuted before. I thought it would be a pity if you were misled by any theory like that, Mr. Prone, so I'm applying also for a summons under the Metropolitan Police Act 1839[2] on the basis of what I've seen today.'

'What you've seen? What are you supposed to have seen?'

'People buying goods from this stall. The Act says you mustn't expose anything for sale upon the footway so as to cause obstruction. See you later on, no doubt.'

And P.C. Flynn passed on his devastating way.

By this time the Prones were past discussing their misfortunes. All day Sunday and Monday they had felt like victims of trench warfare who had been left without ammunition or other means of retaliation. They had merely ducked as each missile came over. Now they began to feel that this was a vast and many-handed practical joke, and that somewhere its decadent authors were delightedly falling about. It was a notion that derived just a little sustenance from what happened later that morning.

Mr. Prone had been much impressed on Sunday evening by the quiet and reassuring response of Mr. Parrott, the solicitor, to the threat of

[1] Children and Young Persons Act 1933, section 18, as amended in 1963 and 1972.
[2] Section 60, sub-section 7.

prosecution under the Indecent Advertisements Act. Such serenity, such confidence and detailed knowledge! And thereafter, as the law trained more and more of its slings and arrows upon the Prone household, he decided that he would refer each new development to the admirable Mr. Parrott, so that at least one responsible and sane person would know (and would later be able to confirm) just what had happened and kept on happening. Monday's most important development had been the loss of his car, which was hardly likely to be restored to him unless he gave the police some kind of undertaking that it would not be used on the road again; or at least that it would not be used without the completion of a programme of repairs costing more than half a dozen vehicles of similar age.

At about eleven o'clock the faithful Mr. Parrott telephoned. He was in fact, as a less agitated Mr. Prone might have realized, fascinated by the developing and unprecedented Prone story; he was percipient enough to see that it must sooner or later become a *cause célèbre*; and he realized that such a story could bring to an otherwise obscure solicitor the publicity reserved as a rule for those with regular letters in *The Times* and regular television appearances offering instant legal punditry. He had been in touch with the police about Mr. Prone's car, he said, and was now able to report that it seemed unlikely there would be prosecutions in respect of it.

Mr. Prone was stunned. 'Do you mind saying that again, slowly?' he said, as he pressed the telephone incredulously to an excited ear. Mr. Parrott told him again that the police were probably not prosecuting, and that he was to listen carefully to the reasons.

'You remember', said Mr.Parrott, 'how the policeman sitting in your passenger's seat told you to drive round the corner and get away from the traffic?'

Mr. Prone did.

'By the way, how far was that, would you think?'

Mr. Prone thought. 'Couple of hundred yards, I suppose', he said.

'I've asked the police this morning,' said Mr. Parrott, 'how many alleged offences they had clocked up against you at that point. It seems there were three. One, driving with defective windscreen wipers. Two, driving without due consideration for other road users (that was when you nearly knocked over the traffic warden). And three, not having your tax disc on the windscreen. I gather, by the way, that the discovery of the defective handbrake came *after* you had driven round the corner? Yes. I managed to get a clear but reluctant admission that the constable who told you to drive round the corner knew when he did so that you would be committing offences in so doing, and committing them under his orders. That applies to the windscreen wipers and the tax disc. It would make them rather worse anyway, because you would no longer be driving in ignorance of them. You would know you were breaking the law—'

'Just a minute', said Mr. Prone. 'Would I really be breaking the law if the constable told me to?'

'You both would. If you had knocked someone down and injured him, perhaps killed him, in the circumstances, your insurance company might well have refused to take any notice of you. That's the bad part of it', said Mr. Parrott. 'What the policeman told you to do would make no difference whatever, except that he would be liable with you—for aiding, abetting, counselling and procuring your offences.'

'Good God', said Mr. Prone.

'Yes. And so I was able to make it plain to the police that your defence would be that you acted under duress. Your car has been taken to a breaker's yard in Everton Street, and you can take over from there. I mean you can either collect it for repair, or leave it for breaking up. Good morning, Mr. Prone, I must hurry.'

When he went out into the shop, Mr. Prone found his wife talking to Mr. Lucas the chemist, who had come in for tobacco. Mr. Lucas was a friend, and a member of the Rotary Club. Mr. Prone told them both about Mr. Parrott's astonishing news, and was slightly nettled that neither of them seemed suitably surprised or excited.

'Well, I mean I never thought from the start they would bother about *all* those things', his wife said. 'And if they've dished themselves by making you drive the car while it wasn't fit to drive, well that's fine isn't it? One up to Mr. Parrott, I say. I mean they could see he would be certain to bring all that out in court. The police would look a bit silly, wouldn't they?'

'I don't know whether your solicitor had this in mind,' said Mr. Lucas the chemist, 'but if the police had insisted on going ahead, you could have prosecuted *them* for aiding and abetting you.'

'*Me* prosecute the police?' said Mr. Prone. 'Don't be daft.' But he suddenly looked wistful.

'Anybody could, if they'd got the evidence. Your wife could. Or me. It doesn't have to be the police who prosecute motorists. People prosecute each other for all sorts of things. But listen: what I was going to say was, I'm going to be away for four days, I've got a trade conference up at Blackpool; and you can have the loan of my Escort van if you want it. Mrs. Prone tells me you can't use yours any more. I'm leaving about eleven o'clock this morning.'

'Mine's gone for break-up', Mr. Prone said. 'I must say I think that's very kind of you, I'm sure. I think I might like to do that. I'm really very grateful. I hope I can do the same for you some time. We must come to an arrangement about the cost.'

'Plenty of time for that. I'll leave it in my side entrance, unlocked; and here's the ignition. Don't forget', called Mr. Lucas over his shoulder, 'to renew your driving licence.'

And he departed, leaving the Prones with the feeling that the world was not, after all, united against them. At least the Rotary movement stood out.

At ten past two Mr. Prone, fumbling a little with the gear lever, was gratefully driving the borrowed van from Spenser Road to Streatham High Road, where he was to inspect a Volkswagen estate car on offer at £520. The advertisement had left him in some doubt whether the place of sale was a dealer's garage or a private house, and as a sceptical buyer of used cars he was relieved to find that it was the former. An hour later he had left a deposit of £50 for the Volkswagen, got a receipt, and was on his way back along Trinity Road. Suddenly a dog ran in front of an approaching cyclist, who swerved violently to avoid it and fell off, at about the right moment for Mr. Prone to run over the bicycle without injuring the cyclist. As usual the bicycle emerged twisted and unusable, and Mr. Prone began looking wearily round for a policeman to whom the details could be supplied, as he thought the law required. It was a memorable feature of Mr. Prone's Tuesday that for once there was no policeman waiting to pounce, though there quickly assembled the inevitable little group of Lowry models, waiting to see whether someone would be arrested or die.

A week earlier Mr. Prone would have been confident that so long as he supplied his name and address to the cyclist, the law laid upon him no obligation to report the accident to the police; and (no one being hurt) he would have been right.[1] This week his confidence was in ruins.

'We ought to tell the police', he said to the cyclist, a boy of about sixteen. And the boy, who was irresolutely holding his misshapen bike, supposed they ought. So Mr. Prone lifted it into the back of the Escort van and they set off together in search of the nearest police station.

'You don't need to report that to us', said the young constable who then listened to their story. 'Are you all right lad?' he asked the boy, who said yes except for his bicycle.

'Well,' said the policeman, seemingly none too resolute himself, 'I

[1] Road Traffic Act 1972, section 25.

suppose I'd better record your call. What's the registration number of your van?'

The horrified Mr. Prone suddenly realized that he didn't know.

'I, er, I don't quite know', he said. 'I'll go out and see.'

Accordingly, the policeman went with him, steering him towards the back number plate, not the front. 'When does the licence expire?' he asked.

'Licence?' said Mr. Prone, miserably gaining time with little hope of being able to use it.

'The tax disc, the thing on the windscreen. I suppose you've got one?'

'Oh yes, yes. Er, I've forgotten the date actually.' (Deep inside Mr. Prone a voice was saying: Tell him it's not yours, you fool. Tell him it's borrowed from a friend. That's the truth, isn't it? Whatever you do, don't start telling lies.)

'Would it be the early part of the year, or near the end perhaps?'

'Oh, er, half-way, about half-way.'

'Like June?'

'Something like that.'

They went and looked. It was December.

'Can you give me evidence of ownership?' (There was now no mistaking the growing suspicion in the policeman's voice.) 'M.O.T. Certificate perhaps? Vehicle Registration Document—what they used to call a log-book? They wouldn't show it was yours, but they'd be a help. No? What about a garage repair bill, something with your name on it?'

Mr. Prone had nothing.

'It's not mine,' he faltered at last, 'it belongs to Mr. Lucas, the chemist in Spenser Road, the other side of Spenser Park.'

'Ah. And he knows you've got it?'

'Of course he knows.'

'We'll go in and 'phone him, shall we? Tell him what's happened?'

They went back into the police station, Mr. Prone once more in the ambiguous position of a reluctant guest uncertain whether it would be a good idea to run away. The constable found Mr. Lucas's telephone number and dialled it. There was a prolonged ringing and no answer. (God, thought Mr. Prone: hope he's told his wife about this, he's not there himself.) Everyone grew impatient, especially the boy whose bicycle was still in the van. 'Don't worry,' Mr. Prone told him, 'I'll run you home.'

'I live at Worthing', said the boy; and Mr. Prone looked at him wanly.

Suddenly there was a female voice on the telephone, audible but not intelligible to everyone; and it told the policeman a number of things that Mr. Prone, in particular, was unable to hear. Something told him that they were unsatisfactory things. The policeman rang off thoughtfully.

'Mr. Lucas is away for four days', he said.

'I KNOW!' shouted Mr. Prone. 'I could have told you that.'

'His wife', the policeman continued, 'says he left his van in the side entrance where it usually stands. She doesn't know anything about him lending it to anyone. We shall have to detain you while we make a few more inquiries.'

'What for?' protested Mr. Prone. 'What am I supposed to have done?'

'The idea at the moment is that you've taken a conveyance, to wit a motor vehicle, for your own use, without having the consent of the owner or other lawful authority.'[1]

'Look,' Mr. Prone said as quietly as he could manage, 'can I use the telephone?'

'Later on, later', said the policeman, who was shepherding Mr. Prone towards an interview room.

'No, not later, *now*. I want to talk to Mrs. Lucas.'

'Who?'

'That lady who answered the 'phone just now. Or you can ring her again yourself if you like. Mr. Lucas lent me his van for four days, and she knows me quite well, even if he forgot to tell her about lending it.'

'Perhaps you'd better give me your name and address?'

And armed with that belatedly-sought information the policeman again spoke to Mrs. Lucas. And this time as he put down the telephone he looked even more thoughtful.

'Well,' he said slowly, 'we'd better get along there so she can identify you.'

And leaving the boy to make arrangements (with a little police help) for the removal of his cycle, they set off for Lucas & Sons, Pharmaceutical Chemists, Spenser Road, South London, the Escort van driven by a policeman and Mr. Prone following anxiously in the back of a police car. Mrs. Lucas soon satisfied the police that, even if her husband hadn't lent Mr. Prone their van, he would probably have done so if asked and she might have considered lending it herself in his absence; and the party could then have broken up, you might have thought, with smiles on all faces except, perhaps, that of Mr. Prone.

Any smile that might have found its way there would, truth to tell, have had a short life. For the purposes of his report the policeman seemed to think it necessary that he should see Mr. Lucas's certificate of insurance. Mrs. Lucas knew just where it was, and got it. As the

[1] Theft Act 1968, section 12.

policeman studied its 'Limitations as to Use' he emitted a long slow
whistle, a sound totally without charm. 'I see this is an O.O.D.', he
said.

'A what?'

'Owner only driving. The van's only insured when Mr. Lucas is
driving it.'

What then saved Mr. Prone from total breakdown was the sudden recollection of what Mr. Parrott had achieved that very morning, in
extricating him from the strangling network of accusations about his
own car and insurance. He drew himself up to his full five feet two.

'So that makes two of us?' he asked. 'Me to drive it to your police
station and you to drive it here? I mean, we're both in the soup, aren't
we? Still, we didn't know. You're no more to blame than I am. Tell
you what, I'll make you an offer.'

'I beg your pardon?'

'You find some way to overlook this business of "Owner Only Driving", and I'll overlook it too,' said Mr. Prone magnanimously. 'But if
you find you can't, I mean if there's some question of prosecuting me
for driving Mr. Lucas's van without being insured, well then I shall
have to prosecute you for doing the same thing, won't I? I don't much
want to do that because I'm very busy, but it's all up to you, if you
understand me?'

Let us now accord him a brief interval (it will be cruelly brief) for the
enjoyment of his tactical triumph, while we recall that it was only yesterday that he discovered himself to be an unlicensed driver. He had not
yet applied for a new licence, and was blissfully unaware that there are
no 'days of grace' for the driver whose licence has expired. His application for the new one must be in the hands of the Secretary of State for
the Environment, or the hands of some lesser but equally trustworthy
person, before the applicant can lawfully drive again.[1] Worse, however,
was to come.

'You probably wouldn't know,' said the policeman, 'but the police
don't have to be insured like that. I can drive any vehicle for police purposes, whether its owner has insured it or not.[2] Perhaps you'd let me
see your driving licence now please?'

All the light went from the face of Mr. Prone. He explained haltingly
that his licence was out of date and that he was applying for a renewal.
'I only knew yesterday', he said.

'How much out of date was it?'

---

[1] Road Traffic Act 1972, section 84 (as amended by the Road Traffic Act 1974,
Schedule 3).
[2] Road Traffic Act 1972, section 144.

'Five weeks', said Mr. Prone in a very low voice indeed.

'So there would be an insurance offence even if this van wasn't limited to "Owner Only Driving"?'

And once again Mr. Prone found himself listening to the news that he would be 'reported for summonses' etc. As soon as this miserable recital was over, he declined a cup of Mrs. Lucas's tea (the policeman was already drinking one) and walked slowly home.

'A young policeman has been here,' Mrs. Prone told him, 'asking for Bruno's licence. Kind of cadet or something, only a boy he looked. I couldn't find it and I said you'd be back soon; so he waited half an hour. But he's gone now.'

'Couldn't find *what*?'

'Bruno's licence. Dog licence. I looked in your filing cupboard or whatever you call it, but I don't know where you keep licences. Tell me about the Volkswagen. Is it all right, and are we having it?'

Mr. Prone had grown silent and broody. He was getting so tired of the word licences. After about two minutes he asked and answered a bitter rhetorical question.

'Why did they send a police cadet to see our dog licence? I'll tell you why. Because P.C. Bloody Flynn forgot to ask me for it, that's why; and then hadn't got the gall to come himself.'

Mrs. Prone asked him again where it was.

'It's in a file marked BIRTHS, DEATHS AND MARRIAGES', he said defiantly. (A man's domestic filing system, where there is one, is his own secret and a clue sometimes to his character.) 'All right, all right, you've got to have somewhere you can find marriage and birth certificates and I reckon a dog licence comes into that sort of thing.'

'And the television licence?'

'What's that got to do with it? I keep that in the . . .' He broke off and hurried to a small drawer labelled PENDING. 'Here it is', and he brandished it triumphantly. She took it from him.

'This says black and white', she said. 'We've had colour since last May or June.'

'We're talking about the dog licence, let's do one thing at a time, shall we? Oh hell, what's the date today?'

'It's the 28th November 1976.'

'This damn thing expired in August. It says I'm "authorised to keep one dog in Great Britain from the date thereof"—that's the 20th August —"until the last day of July next following, the sum of $37\frac{1}{2}$ pence having been paid for this licence". And I've kept one dog in Great Britain since then without any licence at all, and here we are in November. Heigh-ho, more trouble.'

'It's funny you should buy a dog licence on 20th August, that's when we were at Killarney for our holiday. Can I look? It says "Great Britain", that doesn't include Ireland, do you know? I shouldn't have thought you could buy an English dog-licence in an Irish post office anyway. . . . Why, half a minute, this date-stamp is very faint, but it looks to me like 1975, not 1976!'

This is what it was.

'Listen', said the practical Mrs. Prone after the briefest of intervals for consternation (the Prones were getting very experienced). 'There's new people in the post office round the corner. They won't know you and they won't know about Bruno. While I do your sausages for tea, you go and get a new licence for Bruno. The only date on it will be the rubber stamp one, and nobody can ever read those. Don't say it's a *renewal*, mind you.'

The woman whom thou gavest to be with me, he muttered to himself as he waited at the Post Office counter, she gave me of the tree and I did eat. What is this that thou hast done, a rather more frightening voice seemed to be inquiring? And there was no answer. Nor did anyone ask again; P.C. Flynn's police-cadet emissary failed to notice the newness or suspect the relevance of the dog licence. Another corner was safely turned.

After tea Mr. Prone felt rotund and rather more placid. It was astonishing, he thought (wiping his mouth), what misfortunes, buffetings and privations the human spirit could grow accustomed to, and he fortified himself with the thought of Dunkirk, the Blitz, and what else he could remember of the Second World War and How It Was Won. Back in the shop, squaring up to life, he was serving customers almost happily, his service-smile sustaining itself with less difficulty than at any time during the previous three days; and once at least he thought he heard himself humming, without knowing whether he was producing any recognizable tune or what he was supposed to be humming about. The musical interlude was short. Discordantly, the doorbell brought it to a close.

There entered two men who had about them an air of pregnant goodwill, the kind of goodwill that enables a man to know what is best for his fellows. It made Mr. Prone instantly uneasy. Something in their demeanour meant that they were there Only to Help You, and that you had better like it. If the Spenser Park General Stores had been a Wild West store in the 1880s, Mr. Prone would have been reaching unobtrusively for his gun. One man said good afternoon and the other man said they were officers of the Customs and Excise Department. They both then produced cards that seemed to endorse what he had said.

'We have reason', said the second man, 'to believe that you may be evading payment of Value Added Tax on your Outputs.'

'What do you mean, Outputs?' demanded Mr. Prone.

'An Output', said the man, 'is some kind of goods or services supplied by you to somebody else. Tax has to be paid on it—Value Added Tax. You have not been submitting returns of your Outputs and Inputs to the Customs and Excise Department.'

'And do you know why?' demanded Mr. Prone. 'Because I don't know what it's all about. The blasted forms might as well be printed in Persian as far as I'm concerned.'

'Then perhaps we can help you?'

'You *can't* help me.' This was a cantankerous Prone. 'I haven't got the forms here, and if I had I haven't got the time to sit worrying about them.'

'You've mislaid the forms?'

'I didn't say that. I've sent them with all my books to my accountant, he does all this kind of thing, God help him.'

'I see. We haven't heard anything from you, or from him, since February, that's nine months. Why is that, Mr. Prone?'

'It could be because he doesn't understand them either, or it could be because a lot of other people like me are asking him to help them. What's an Output?'

'I've just told you that, or tried to. Outputs, in your case, are the things you sell.'

'Well, why the hell do you have to call them Outputs? Outputs to me could be the empty cartons and Coke tins I shove outside for the dustman.'

The VAT man was ominously patient. 'What do you call the things you sell, Mr. Prone?'

'Goods, I call them.'

'And what about a shoemender or a hairdresser? Are *they* selling goods?'

Mr. Prone sniffed.

'I don't understand it all,' he said, 'and I don't agree with it. All I'm trying to do is make a living. All this form-filling sends me up the creek, without having people like you coming in and saying I'm breaking the law.'

'You probably keep your invoices filed away somewhere, do you? I mean invoices for the goods you buy?'

'I do, yes.'

'Filed alphabetically?'

'No, they're filed in boxes according to the kind of goods. Well, I change to a new supplier quite often; anyway, more often than I change the kind of things I buy and sell.'

'So perhaps you'll show me the box-files, will you?'

Mr. Prone glared at him.

'You tell me why I should.'

'Because section 37 of the Finance Act 1972 empowers me to inspect your premises at any reasonable time and also to inspect your goods.'

'Does it now? Well, suppose the files are not here—say they're at the accountant's?'

'Oh but they are not, are they? Your accountant wouldn't need all those details at this stage; if he wanted those he would come here for them. Perhaps you'll just show me where they are?'

'I will not', said Mr. Prone, quaking with defiance.

'So what that means, you see, is that we shall have to search the premises for them.'

'You just show me what authority you've got for doing that. Go on, show me.'

'Mr. Prone, if we find it necessary to search the premises I shall need to get a search warrant from a magistrate.'[1] There was a deprecating cough. 'But I must tell you that if it comes to that we might find it necessary to search this place very thoroughly, from top to bottom, and not merely the shop.'

By this time Mr. Prone was finding, as he sometimes did, that language was an imperfect means of communicating ideas, and he was looking for some blunt instrument. Rare as it was in her husband, Mrs. Prone recognized this as a symptom calling for prompt action.

'I'll telephone Mr. Shackleford,' she said hurriedly, 'and ask him to come round at once. That's our accountant', she explained to the VAT man. 'He can clear everything up, I'm *quite* sure. And while we're waiting for him,' she said comfortably, 'we can have a good strong cup of tea and quieten down a bit.'

Mr. Shackleford arrived with a reassuring expression and a bulging brief case. There had clearly been a mistake, he said. VAT returns concerning Mr. Prone's business had been submitted in May and July, each with a number of queries to be cleared up before the appropriate cheques were sent off.

'Have you got Mr. Prone's box-files of invoices?' he was asked.

[1] Finance Act 1972, section 37(3).

He had not. Nor did he know where they were. But if the VAT man wanted to see them, he had no doubt they could be produced on due notice.

'These busy shopkeepers', said Mr. Shackleford, 'simply have no time to read and understand all this stuff. I do several lots of accounts round here. I used to do their Income Tax only, but now with this VAT as well it all takes a lot longer.'

'So which is the right explanation, that it all takes a long time or that Mr. Prone's May and July returns have gone astray somewhere?'

Mr. Shackleford's eyes diminished in area. 'That we shall have to find out, shan't we?' he said.

The inspector turned to Mr. Prone. 'You just don't understand VAT forms at all?' he said.

'I don't know what they're all about, or why they've been foisted on us', said Mr. Prone angrily. 'They don't use the kind of language I know. Just look at this.' He snatched from a drawer a booklet bearing the legend *V.A.T. News.* In its top right-hand corner was a little drawing of a portcullis, with strong chains by which it could be pulled up and then dropped, spikes downwards, on the bodies of taxpayers trying to scramble in or out.

'I get these four times a year', he said. 'I've got dozens of them. I used to try and read them at first. Now I keep them in the loo. I don't understand a word they say. 'NOTES ON THE TOLERANCE IN PARTIAL EXEMPTION ADJUSTMENTS'—what the hell does *that* mean?'

'You can never make a man understand what he doesn't want to understand, Mr. Prone. I think you're not really quite so dense as this. These notes are devised—'

'And just listen to this,' said Mr. Prone, who had been turning the pages and not listening:

'Most persons using authorised special methods relate inputs directly to either taxable or exempt outputs as far as possible and apportion only the tax on inputs which cannot be directly related to either (residual input tax), such as overhead expenses common to both sides of the business (see paragraph 8 of Notice No. 706).'

'I don't see any purpose in prolonging a discussion like this', said the Customs man. 'If you have submitted VAT returns that we have not received, perhaps you could let us have duplicates. Here are some extra forms. For the moment we will leave it at that. Good afternoon.'

Mr. Shackleford said good afternoon and, until the shop door closed,

Mr. Prone said nothing. Then Mr. Prone said, 'Why can't these people go to some language school and learn the kind of language we all understand?'

'It all has to be very carefully explained,' Mr. Shackleford said, 'and the terms they use have to apply to hundreds of different kinds of businesses.'

'Does that stop them using commas and things? Can't they punctuate? Both my kids know how to punctuate. It's not an Act of Parliament, for lawyers to earn their living on. It's supposed to be a guide for the ordinary bloke. If they can't do it why don't they farm it out to someone who can? Some P.R. or advertising firm? Or somebody like the Consumer Association—cor, I bet they could do it. Or they could set a competition for schoolkids with a prize for the best effort. Why, I could do it better myself', said Mr. Prone with fortuitous modesty.

'I remember you saying that about the old Income Tax form,' said Mr. Shackleford, 'before they simplified it.'

'SIMPLIFIED! When was that? I tell you, Mr. Shackleford, there's hardly anybody understands the thing, and this so-called Tax Return Guide they send with it, why I've just had to give it up, chuck it up in despair.'

When Mr. Shackleford had gone, Mrs. Prone had a few cautionary words to address to her exasperated husband.

'We mustn't let Mr. Shackleford think we know *nothing* about these forms and what's required', she said. 'That's putting temptation in his way. . . . Good afternoon', she said to a customer who had just come in. What would you like sir?'

Mr. Prone's trade in confectionery was almost a juvenile monopoly: lollies, Smarties, gob-stoppers, jelly-babies, liquorice allsorts, and aniseed balls; but wrapped toffees, boiled sweets, and chewing gum were available in small quantities for the more advanced citizen. The very occasional demand for a box of chocolates, prompted as it usually was by eleventh-hour attacks of impromptu generosity or guilty propitiation, had led him to keep in stock (when he thought of it) a few large and ornate flat boxes of the more expensive assorted chocolates. Three such boxes usually stood on a high shelf near the door, an important part of the general decor but too high for regular dusting. On this Tuesday afternoon a young man with a capacious carrier-bag came in and asked Mrs. Prone for a head of celery. Now celery, when she had it, she displayed in a box outside, and she went out to get some. The doorbell, recording her exit, made Mr. Prone look up from counting the newly-arrived evening papers, and he thought he saw one of the large chocolate boxes disappearing into the young man's carrier-bag. A glance at the high display shelf confirmed that one of the impressive three was missing; and Mr. Prone, picking up a quire of evening papers, moved round to the shop door with an artful display of unconcern that owed much to the forensic experience of the past three days. Then, having quickly shut the door, he turned the key and put it in his pocket.

'Closing time already?' said the young man, with a glance at his wrist-watch.

And Mrs. Prone, returning with the celery, was at the same moment registering and conveying her indignation, through the glass panel, that the door wouldn't open.

'What about that box of chocolates?' Mr. Prone demanded.

'I agree', said the young man with staggering calm. 'What about it?' He lifted it half out of his carrier-bag and let it fall back again. 'I really wanted some chocolate ginger, but this will do, I suppose.'

'Oh, will it? And what about paying for it?'

'Paying? Whatever do you mean? I haven't finished buying yet, have I? Why not open the door for this lady?'

Instead Mr. Prone shouted to his wondering wife, to whom he was just audible through the closed door. 'Get the police!' was what he shouted. 'Go in next door and ask to use Mr. Whiffen's phone. Eh? Tell Mr. Whiffen it's shoplifting, stealing, theft, I've got a man here I want arrested.'

And Mrs. Prone hurried obediently away, celery in hand.

'Now, I'll trouble you to return that box of chocolates.'

'All right, if you really don't want to sell them. Here it is, actually I wouldn't take it now as a gift. If you're thinking of getting the police in on this scene, you will be making a great big mistake, I can tell you that free of charge.'

Meanwhile a knot of intending customers had gathered outside the locked door, puzzled by the spectacle on the other side of the glass of Mr. Prone engrossed in apparently angry conversation with a man who (according to Mrs. Prone) had merely wanted some celery. This cameo lasted some minutes and its cast was then reinforced, first by the return of Mrs. Prone and Mr. Whiffen from the radio shop next door, and then by the crew of a police patrol car who had arrived with radio-directed and commendable promptness. A policeman tapped on the glass door-panel, looked inquiringly through at Mr. Prone, and was admitted.

And then to the constable, to Mrs. Prone and Mr. Whiffen, and to those of the little crowd who had been lucky enough to get in before the police closed the door again, Mr. Prone told his story. It was promptly contested with such convincing scorn by the young man with the carrier-bag that even Mr. Prone began to have doubts himself. But about these he kept carefully and uneasily quiet, for reasons which must now be revealed.

A month or so before this story opened, a woman had stolen from a rack outside the shop two pounds of potatoes in a polythene bag. Mr. Prone and the small shopkeepers of the neighbourhood had lately agreed among themselves, in contrast to some of the supermarkets, that all shoplifting offences were to be prosecuted, whatever the police thought about it; for what the police had seemed to think lately was that it was a waste of everyone's time to prosecute in cases involving less than £5. Police interest, therefore, in the two pounds of potatoes had at first been confined to obtaining for Mr. Prone the lady's name and address, so that he could, if he wished to do so as a private citizen, obtain a magistrate's summons against her to answer a charge of theft. But for some reason the police had then changed their minds, and it had been at their instance that she had appeared in court a fortnight ago and was remanded for two weeks, being granted both bail and Legal Aid. It so happened that the adjourned hearing was to take place on the morning after the episode of the young man with the carrier-bag, the head of celery, and the big box of chocolates. As to which, the police were even less encouraging.

'I'm afraid it's not a case for the police, really', the constable told Mr. Prone. 'If you want to proceed against this man you will have to try and convince a magistrate that he intended to steal the chocolates, and it looks to me a bit difficult.'

'But I saw them in his bag! *And* I saw him putting them in. Why would he put them in there, if he meant to pay for them?'

'I deny they were in my bag or any bag', said the young man unexpectedly and shatteringly. 'I had them under my arm and was waiting to pay.'

'Officer, he purposely asked my wife for something he saw *outside* the shop, so he could be on his own inside for half a minute. He reckoned he had the shop to himself—it's what they all do. He didn't see me because I was behind the book-rack counting the evening papers. I knew what he was up to all right. You should have seen his face when I suddenly appeared—that's enough evidence for anybody.'

'Only for you, I'm afraid. You've got no witnesses, you see, and he can say he was still buying things. It would be different if he'd left the shop without paying. But here's his name and address for you. .. Have you made up your mind to apply for a summons?'

'Look, I called you because I want to give him in charge, I want him arrested. This isn't just suspicion, I *saw* him do it.'

'Sorry Mr. Prone. Perhaps you'll let us know, for the record, if you decide to go ahead with it. Good afternoon.'

And as the police car left the scene, the still suspected but still unruffled young man laid the chocolate box on the shop counter, placed the celery on top of it, dusted his hands together, and walked quietly away.

Mr. Prone was again restless that night.'I've got to be in the Magistrates' Court anyway in the morning,' he said, 'and judging by this affair today it's going to be a right waste of time.'

'Can't be', said his wife. 'That woman was caught red-handed, *and* we've got four witnesses.'

'Yes, and they've all been to court once already, fortnight ago. Hung about most of the day, all over two pounds of spuds. I've given my promise to the Chamber of Trade that I'll prosecute shoplifters, but I'm not looking forward to it. Damn waste of time.'

'That's what the police say', said his wife.

And the next day the Prones were going to consider this an understatement.

Wednesday

'LETTER from Tom Drake again,' said Mr. Prone, 'about his fingers.' He snorted. 'Wish I'd never employed that man, he's accident-prone.'

Mrs. Prone tipped a little more porridge into his plate. 'That's a bit rich, coming from you,' she said, 'in the middle of a week like this. Prone by name, prone by nature, that's you. How long did we employ him?'

'About seven months. All he did most of that time was fall down or bang his head on things. He's reported that window-cleaning affair to the Department of Health and Social Security, and I suppose that means more trouble.'

Tom Drake was a piece of social flotsam, a rather cumbersome and slow-moving piece, whom the Prones had employed experimentally as a general handyman and messenger in pursuance of a Rotary Club scheme for rehabilitating discharged prisoners. He had left two months ago, at Mr. Prone's invitation, because of a consistent shortage of cigarettes which had begun soon after his arrival and continued until he left. But shortly before he did this, as a kind of climax to a series of household accidents in which he had been the central and sometimes bloodstained figure, he was cleaning a sash-window on the first-floor landing when the sash cord broke and the lower half of the window crushed his fingers. This made it the more difficult to tell him he must go, but he was already under notice and the fingers seemed an inadequate reason for telling him that, after all, he could stay. The sequel had been a correspondence with the Department of Health and Social Security on the subject of industrial injury and the liabilities of employers.

Mr. Prone had barely finished his breakfast, indeed, when a man came into the shop, declared himself to be an official of that Department, and rather abruptly introduced the subject of Tom Drake's fingers. Could he see the window involved in the accident? (He took out a note-book.) The broken sash cord was still hanging loose, but the official lifted the window and let it go, at some risk of breaking the glass but as if to convince himself that any fingers in its way would get hurt.

'No doubt', he said, 'you've got a record of the accident? An accident book perhaps? No? Merely a sheet of paper would do, it doesn't have to be a book.'

Mr. Prone glumly revealed that there was no written record of any kind, on anything.

'Oh dear', said the man from the Department of Health and Social Security. 'I'm afraid the failure to make such a record is an offence under the Social Security Act of 1975. So is the failure to produce such a record to me.'

'Don't be daft', said Mr. Prone. 'How the devil can I produce a record that doesn't exist?'

'I know, that's what I often wonder', said the official. 'Seems unfair, doesn't it? And a bit like having two bites at a cherry. Still, the magistrates will usually decide not to convict on both.'

'Magistrates?' spluttered Mr. Prone. 'You mean to say I get prosecuted because that useless clot has hurt his fingers?'

'No, no, it's because you failed to make a record of it and therefore can't produce one to me. No doubt you will be hearing more about it shortly. Good morning.'

Another day had started. The episode with the Man from the Ministry
had almost made Mr. Prone forget that he was due at the Magistrates'
Court that morning, to continue his prosecution of one Mrs. Martha
Jones for the theft of two pounds of potatoes. Martha Jones and her
swarming family were didicois; that is to say, although they were natural
wanderers they were not gypsies but they would have liked everyone to
think they were. The derelict piece of scrubland on which their tumble-
down caravan had long rested, not far from the gates of Spenser Park,
had once been a gypsy encampment; but not within the memory of any
resident in the neighbourhood. More than once the police, prompted by
the local authority (prompted by exasperated neighbours), had half-
heartedly made as if to remove the Jones family and their caravan, but
it was always found that the wheels of the latter had long passed their
revolving days, and indeed that although the structure rested on things
that looked like wheels, it might as well have been on piles driven deep
into the ground.

It was known among the local shopkeepers that Martha was a thief,
and it had been decided among them that for much too long everyone
had been too kind to her, as a sort of folksy landscape figure. (She was
known to the local children as the old-woman-who-lived-in-a-shoe.)
Once it was generally realized that her system of shopping did not include the usual courtesies at the cash desk on the way out, it was agreed
that she must be prosecuted at the next opportunity; and it was the next
opportunity that had involved Mr. Prone and his two pounds of potatoes. There had been an adjournment of two weeks because the police
had intimated, after an initial unwillingness to prosecute at all, that
'inquiries were proceeding and not yet complete', by which they really
meant that they hoped she would admit the authorship of a great number of similar thefts and ask for them to be 'taken into consideration'
when she was sentenced. She had begun by admitting several of these in
conversation with the police, and then, when confronted with the necessary forms of signature, had taken fright and withdrawn everything she
had said. She was still pleading Not Guilty, and her young Legal Aid
solicitor was prepared to fight the case as if it were one of mass murder.

The police were not represented by a solicitor, and when Martha's
case was called on it was a detective sergeant who stepped forward to
say that he was regretfully unable to add anything to what the Court
had been told at the previous hearing.

'Does that mean', said the Magistrates' Clerk, 'that this adjournment
has been totally unproductive and a waste of everyone's time?'

It did, and for a reason which was to increase even further Mr.
Prone's now chronic state of dismay.

'Where is the owner of the goods?' asked the Magistrates' Clerk. 'The er, potatoes? The shopkeeper?'

'He doesn't seem to be here, sir.'

'Then where is he?'

No one knew. Clerk and magistrates mumblingly conferred.

'See if he's in the building somewhere', said the Magistrates' Clerk to the uniformed warrant officer. 'He should have been here at ten-thirty.'

Poor Mr. Prone had clearly understood it to be eleven o'clock. But while the search for him is in progress, and while in fact he is on his way by bus to the Court, it may be of interest to recall why it is that so many offenders, with so abject an appearance of remorse, ask for great numbers of other offences to be 'taken into consideration' in passing sentence, offences of which the police sometimes would otherwise have known nothing. Is it that police officers have brainwashed or bullied them into a shamefaced realization of their treachery to the State, to the Nation, to the people's revolution, to the fatherland?

It is not.

The system began, or at least was given High Court recognition, in 1908 and was an early product of the newly established Court of Criminal Appeal.[1] Its main effect is to 'clean the slate' for a prisoner being sentenced, who in former days could be repeatedly rearrested at the prison gates as he came out on discharge, to be repeatedly charged with offences traced to or admitted by him. When he has been convicted he can now be asked, by the judge or magistrate but by no one else, whether he admits the list of 'outstanding charges' alleged against him. If he doesn't, they must be ignored. If he does, he can be given a sentence that purports to take them all into account. It is usually a good bargain for him: in fact he seldom comes off much worse than if he had kept quiet about his past; and it is nice for the police, who are able to record a whole list of crimes as 'cleared up', so that in the annual *Criminal Statistics, England and Wales*, it looks as though they were all instances of successful police inquiry, detection, even bravery.[2]

Mr. Prone got there at ten-fifty, looking relatively unconcerned, and

---

[1] *R. v. Syres*, 1908, 1 Cr. App. Rep. 171.

[2] Sometimes the police are sorely tempted to persuade a man to admit to crimes he knows absolutely nothing about, thus 'clearing up' some intractable mysteries at little or no cost to a complaisant old lag. Sometimes an old lag even offers to do a little clearing up for them, asking, in effect, if they have any unsolved crimes on their minds to which they would care to put his name; in return for which, by implication, they might be able to leave unsaid some of the nastier things they must otherwise place before the court. But this is dangerous because the truth, even about an old lag, has a way of suddenly and belatedly making itself known in a verifiable statement by some other prisoner in a totally unrelated case, to the embarrassment of all and the benefit of none.

made his way to the court room. There he asked a policeman about the case of Mrs. Martha Jones.

'All over?' said Mr. Prone indignantly. 'What do you mean, all over? It comes on at eleven o'clock. Martha Jones, the name's Martha Jones, stealing.'

It took some time to convince him that he had made a mistake about the time; and then he was ushered into court, where another trial was just beginning. This, said the policeman who gently pushed him forward, was Mr. Percival Prone, the missing prosecutor. The magistrate glared at him.

'Why were you not here at ten-thirty?' he demanded.

'I thought we began at eleven o'clock', grumbled Mr. Prone. 'The police told me eleven o'clock.'

'The case has been dismissed', said the chairman, 'for want of prosecution. If you can't get here on time and everyone else can, you must take the consequences. The case has been dismissed with costs against the prosecution.'

And a speechless Mr. Prone, weighed down and silenced by the burden of lateness, was led from the court.

'So she gets away with it?' he spluttered to the police inspector outside in a corridor.

'She gets away with it. Seems a bit odd to me, I must say. High-handed. That magistrate was late himself last Tuesday, kept us all waiting about twenty minutes.'

'And what's this about costs against the prosecution? Who pays those? Me? Whose costs?'

'Well, there's the expenses of your four witnesses, all coming twice to court. Loss of time, cost of fares, petrol, all that.'

'Do you mean I have to pay those, just because I was told the wrong time?'

'I don't know who told you the wrong time, but the costs will probably be paid out of Central Funds. It's lucky for you the police took the case on.'

'And what about *my* loss of time? I reckon this case has cost me about twenty quid at the least, as a self-employed person. Do I get *that* back?'

'You'd be lucky', said the inspector, permitting himself a broad grin. The police, Mr. Prone gathered, would see to it that his four witnesses were not out of pocket, but his own pecuniary loss seemed to be something he must bear himself. Mr. Prone lost his temper.

'That woman', he shouted passionately, and his voice rang through the tiled corridors, 'has got more money than I have. How the devil did she get Legal Aid, anyway? Everyone knows she's a horse-coper, she's got ponies tethered on all the commons round here for miles—'

'Are you talking about my client?' said her youthful solicitor, pausing on his way out of the building. 'I think you had better be very careful indeed.' And as Mr. Prone watched him leave the building, his jaws were opening and shutting silently, as they did when his vocabulary failed.

Mr. Prone's mood, back at the shop, was not communicative. He told his wife, in the briefest possible terms, that Martha had been found Not Guilty; which was not at all what had happened. But then he telephoned his grief and bewilderment to Mr. Parrott the solicitor, and Mrs. Prone, listening intently from the shop whenever she could, overheard most of the story. After the 'phone call, he seemed slightly comforted. But not for long.

'I *thought* it was 10.30', she said, as wives always do. 'I'm sure you told me 10.30 after that first hearing. I told you didn't I? How did you come to think it was 11 o'clock? I didn't like to go on about it too much.' But she showed unmistakable signs of catching up.

The conversation thus introduced was acrimonious, and he was glad to escape from it and eat a solitary lunch in the shop-parlour. Even so, he had to be brusque and resolute. As he sat down to the meal she placed before him, she hovered for a moment as if with something else to say before returning to the shop. 'There was one other thing', she said hesitantly, 'that I ought to tell you about.' But he thought he foresaw further developments of the theme already stated in the overture, and with his mouth already full he waved her away. Nothing could illustrate more poignantly the effect of these past four days upon a man normally kind to women and good at listening. Mr. Parrott, thank God, had been reassuring: the magistrates were wrong, Mr. Parrott had said, and if Mr. Prone could drop in about seven that evening he would tell him why.

But then Mr. Prone, who had not yet had time to open the morning's mail, pushed away his rapidly emptied pudding plate and began opening letters. The second one was headed 'In the County of London, Petty Sessional Division of Mitcham: Attachment of Earnings Act 1971', and its signatory was 'J. Bolton, Clerk to the Justices'. Its purpose was to remind Mr. Prone that he had recently employed one Thomas Drake, who was 'required to pay a sum, namely £100, to which section 1(3)(b) of the Attachment of Earnings Act 1971 applied' and which Mr. Prone had been ordered, as the said Thomas Drake's employer, to withhold from him as 'periodical deductions in accordance with Schedule 3 to the Act until the amount of that sum remaining unpaid, namely £90, has been deducted.'

Mr. J. Bolton went on to say that these periodical payments had fallen into arrears and that he would be glad to hear from Mr. Prone; who, he added, was liable to a fine of £25 if he failed to comply with the order; one kind of failure being the omission to notify Mr. J. Bolton if Tom Drake was no longer employed at the shop. And the notifying must be done within ten days of Tom's departure.

'That £100 fine was for his last offence,' said Mrs. Prone, 'when he expected to go to prison again. Stealing a woman's purse, he told me.'

'I forgot all about the bloke', said Mr. Prone. 'And now I suppose I'm for it, because I didn't notify the court that I'd sacked him. I didn't do that because I thought the police would come wanting to know why he was sacked, and then there'd be all the business about the missing cigarettes, I've had enough of that kind of thing. And so this is what you get for trying to help a man when he's down. This so-called "attachment of earnings" is just a way of making employers like me do the work of the magistrates.'

'Is that *their* job then, collecting fines?' said Mrs. Prone innocently, but it was not a good thing to say.

'Well, the police', Mr. Prone muttered, conditioned by now to believe that the police did everything. 'Anyhow it's just a way of getting a man back into prison when there's people like me trying to keep him out.'

'Sometimes,' said his wife, 'I don't think you're very reasonable, do you know that? Specially when you're wanting to feel a bit sorry for yourself. If he won't pay his fine and you forget to take it out of his pay, what else is there but prison? You know what *I* thought about employing that man anyway.'

Mr. Prone said he supposed he must tell Mr. Parrott about it and take his advice. It all looked like producing another summons from the magistrates, whatever happened. How many would that be? The Prones had lost count.

'I'm going to call at Mr. Parrott's house this evening when I've collected the Volkswagen', he told his wife. 'I'll tell him then.'

She turned and stared at him. 'Really?' she said. 'Couldn't be better. Can I come? It's just what I wanted', she added mysteriously.

That Wednesday afternoon had looked like being a relatively uneventful interlude of retail trading and shopmanship, and here once more was Mrs. Prone saying, 'There's another thing I wanted to tell you, only at lunch time you didn't want to listen.'

'I know,' he said, 'it's what you wanted to talk about before. I suppose it's Sheila Best? That's simple. If she won't be coming any more we must get someone else, mustn't we? It's only for the early mornings.'

'It's not that. We need someone all day, not just early mornings.'

'WHAT? All day? Not another Tom Drake? I've had enough of handymen.'

'We need a girl, a young woman, in the shop. We've made Susan do it when she could, but it's not right, she's got her exams to work for.'

Mr. Prone felt like a man being urged to pull another passenger into a dinghy full of water.

'How much would we have to pay her?' he said slowly.

'Not so much as you paid Tom Drake for doing practically nothing. Less than a grown man's wage. And I've had an idea—I could easily pay for her myself; it's what I've been trying to tell you about all day. Listen. Mr. and Mrs. Darling are giving up their house and going into a bungalow in Wiltshire, and they don't want to breed those Jack Russells any more. They know I love Jack Russells and they've offered me their three breeding bitches at £5 each, it's ridiculous really, they're worth I should think £50 at least. And one of them's already in whelp.'

Mr. Prone was silent.

'Those puppies', she went on, 'sell at £25 each, often a lot more. I think I could make hundreds of pounds a year.'

She paused again, to find that the silence was still going on.

'Anyway I've said I'll buy them and I wondered if we could collect them in the Volkswagen this evening—there's three kennels as well, you see.'

'You've set your heart on it, haven't you? All right then, I suppose, and if you'll do all the work—I mean I'm not much good with dogs, even old Bruno is more than I want sometimes.'

It was done.

At seven o'clock they were with Mr. Parrott, who (speaking from notes) repeated to them the story of Martha Jones and the potatoes, to see if he had got it right. He had.

'Then I think you could challenge this', said Mr. Parrott, 'in the Queen's Bench Division. It's exactly contrary to the unanimous decision of the Lord Chief Justice, Mr. Justice Donaldson, and Mr. Justice Boreham in *The Queen* v. *Uxbridge Justices, ex parte Frederick Smith*.'[1]

Mr. Prone's eyes gleamed and Mrs. Prone's looked up at the ceiling. 'The Uxbridge magistrates had dismissed a case "for want of prosecution" with £50 costs against the police, because the main police witness

[1] 1977 Road Traffic Reports 93.

was fifteen minutes late when the case was called on. And the judges sent
the case back to them with instructions to try it properly.'

'So what do I do?'

'You decide first of all whether you think you can afford to risk more
money on it. If you can, we tell the magistrates we think they were
wrong in law and we ask them to "state a case" for the consideration of
the High Court, explaining what they did and why they did it.'

'How much does that cost?'

'Very little so far. The cost comes in the High Court proceedings,
where the magistrates will be represented by solicitor and counsel, and
so will you, and if the case goes against you again—'

'WHAT! Goes against me? If the magistrates have got their law
wrong, how *can* the judges go against me?'

'Oh, they may decide the magistrates have got their law right. I don't
think so, mind you, but it's always a dicey business. If you were a
wealthy man or some big corporation, you'd probably be raring to go
on to the Court of Appeal, even perhaps to the House of Lords.'

'What, over a couple of pounds of spuds?'

'It might be an important principle, you see, affecting all your future
business; worth a great deal of expense to you.'

'Well it isn't, Mr. Parrott. What would it cost just to go to the High
Court, and no further?'

'Possibly £200, if it fell to you to pay the costs.'

Mr. Prone stared at him transfixed.

'And no Legal Aid?'

'Very doubtful, I should say. I have to advise you that the Legal Aid
Committee would be unlikely to think the point of sufficient importance
for the expenditure of so much public money.'

'Well they can keep it', said Mr. Prone angrily and finally. 'But is that
what they call justice? I mean you're a lawyer, what do you think of it?'

'One has always to apply certain broad principles—'

'I know—"On the one hand this, on the other hand that"—I wish I
could find a one-armed lawyer. I mean that woman pinched my potatoes, everyone knows she's a thief, and I'm about £20 worse off already,
as well as the spuds, all because of a genuine mistake about the time of
the trial.'

'I know just how you feel.'

'What if the police had turned me down, I mean refused to take the
case on (that's what they wanted to do at first), and I'd decided to
prosecute that woman on my own, and got you to act for me? I suppose
I would have had to pay your fee then, all for nothing. Right?'

'Wrong', said Mr. Parrott. 'The result would have been quite different.'

'Why should it be any different?'

'I wouldn't have been fifteen minutes late,' Mr. Parrott said with a wicked little grin, 'and I should have seen to it that all my witnesses knew the exact time of the court hearing.'

It took an hour to collect the three Jack Russell bitches, pay for them, receive their pedigree certificates and their licences, and arrange them (each in her own kennel) in the luggage space of the newly-acquired Volkswagen. It took another hour to instal them in the crowded little yard behind the shop. And both operations took heavy toll of Mr. Prone's patience and rather perfunctory love of animals. But at last it was all done, and it was then that the noise began, a barking and howling that completely drowned the more formal observations contributed throughout by Bruno the Labrador. The three Jack Russells started up at about a quarter to ten; and showed signs (which proved only too reliable) of continuing all through the night.

Mrs. Prone was at great pains not to notice the noise and, above all, not to appear to notice it. There remained one or two other matters that must be communicated and explained to her husband before the end of the day, and although she would gladly have postponed their narration until the next morning, something told her that the next day was likely to carry its own burden of sorrow and that there would be no room in it for anything retrospective. She set about preparing the pot of strong tea with which, whatever else might happen, the Prones rounded off each evening before going up to bed; and as she passed between her now exhausted husband and the television news he had settled to watch with his customary apathy, she stopped and turned up the volume. He stirred in his easy chair.

'That's a bit loud, isn't it?' he said. 'I'm not deaf, but that's the way to bring it on.'

'I can't hear it from the kitchen', she said, and what she meant was that she didn't want him to hear the howling of the Jack Russells. She bustled with extra ceremony about the making of the tea. Nothing, in the Prone household, could compare with a good strong cup of tea as a solace in the kind of further revelations to which her husband was about to be subjected. (There are conventional people, it is said, to whom it would seem low and even barbarous to drink tea at bedtime, while others deprecate the drinking of tea at all. They do not understand about tea and the shopkeeping bourgeoisie, and it is a lack of understanding I wish there were more time to dispel. Even Mr. J. B. Priestley, who of all men should know better, has said: 'Our trouble is that we drink too much tea. I see in this the slow revenge of the Orient, which has diverted the Yellow River down our throats.'[1] Mrs. Prone would have found strength and comfort in the warmer-hearted counsel of Mr. Anthony Burgess: 'The best thing to do when you've got a dead body and it's your husband's on the kitchen floor, and you don't know what to do about it, is to make yourself a good strong cup of tea.')[2]

Mrs. Prone's husband, moreover, was still stubbornly alive though battered; and as the sipping ritual began, she introduced the first of the day's remaining news items.

'The Health Inspector came again today', she said.

Mr. Prone stiffened.

'He said he wanted to have the usual quick look round', she continued. 'It was during the morning.'

He got up and turned off the television sound, leaving only a silently mouthing news-reader to serve as a focus and refuge for the eyes of worried men. Mrs. Prone continued.

'First he wanted to know why the crate of fresh milk was on the floor. Said it ought to be put straight in the cooling cabinet. Then he asked for our milk licence and said it was out of date. Expired last year, December I think it was.'

'Surprised you knew where to find that', growled Mr. Prone. 'I can't remember when I saw it last. Renewal comes round every four years.'

'Yes, I asked him why they didn't send us a reminder, and he said they could never cope with all the work.'

'Cope?' said Mr. Prone. 'Work? They cope with about thirteen million drivers' licences, and *they* all get reminders, don't they?'

'It's not the same people.'

'It's THEM, as far as I'm concerned', said Mr. Prone. 'Anything else? You've got something else you want to tell me, haven't you? Come on.'

'It's the ice-cream.'

'Ice-cream? What about it?'

'When the Health Inspector came in, two kids were buying choc-ices and he said he "wasn't aware that we were registered with the local authority for the sale of ice-cream", just like that. Well, I wasn't aware either.'

'You see, I just can't turn my back can I? If I'd been here I could have told him about that.'

'You know where the licence is?'

'No no, there's no licence, it's just a registration. You get a sort of certificate, well it's a letter really, saying you've duly registered the

---

[1] *The Observer*, 15 May 1949.
[2] *One Hand Clapping*, 1961.

premises as selling ice-cream, so that they know it's a place where they
can come snooping. It's a once-for-all thing, it was done before we took
this place over. That's all right, I can show them this place is registered,
even if they can't find that it is. I'll have another cup if there is one.'

'Oh that's all right then I suppose. Well, then Jimmy was home from
school for his dinner and he'd caught a butterfly.' Mrs. Prone then took
a rashly generous mouthful of very hot tea and was unable to go on for
a brief interval. Brief as it was, Mr. Prone made unhappy and excited
use of it.

'Oh no!' he almost shouted. 'Do I have to get a licence because my
boy catches *butterflies*? That's just about all it takes. Right: now it's
going to be *my* turn, I'm going to take up this business of never-ending
licences for this and that and the other—'

'Do you mind?' said his wife. 'You've got licences on the brain. Who
said anything about butterfly licences? Perhaps you'll let me finish what
I was saying. I was serving a customer with some of those home-made
cakes from Jackson's, and I'd put down the cake-cover on the other
counter—you know, the big Perspex cover. The Health Inspector
wasn't here then. Well in comes Jimmy with his butterfly in a match-
box and he picks up the cake-cover—I never saw it go, I was busy—and
takes it into the parlour. Next I know he's got it on the table and this
poor thing fluttering about underneath it.'

'Good God', observed Mr. Prone.

'I know. So of course it has to be about then that this wretched Health
Inspector comes in and he wants to know why the cakes aren't covered.'

'Now he's asked me that before,' said Mr. Prone in his voice of
martyrdom, 'and yet if you go into any of the big shops, or some of the
small ones come to that, you can see cakes uncovered all over the place,
even in the summer with the flies all over them. So there's more trouble
about that I suppose?'

'Oh, he said we must take it as a caution, and the ice-cream he was
going to look into, and we must keep the cakes covered. Mind you, I
think he's quite right myself, I was very cross with Jimmy, he's a bad
boy to go off with the cake-cover like that, he knows perfectly well what
it's for.'

'Heigh-ho, well if that's all I'll give Bruno a run and then let's get
to bed. Is there *nothing* you can do about those dogs? Thank God we
sleep in the front.'

Now Bruno the Labrador was a strong and eager dog, and by the
time his old leather lead had been taken down from its hook behind the
kitchen door and Mr. Prone had put on his raincoat, the excitement of
these unmistakable preliminaries had stoked up his strength to the point

where it was Mr. Prone, not Bruno, who was taken for a walk. As they went along Spenser Road they were leaning in opposite directions, Bruno forward, his master backward; and they had gone no more than fifty yards when, just as Mr. Prone was anxiously thinking for the hundredth time of his intention to buy a stout dog-chain, the strap broke, close to the collar. Bruno, deeming it unnecessary to find out whether this sudden release was official or accidental, was off at top speed along Spenser Road before Mr. Prone could draw breath to whistle. And when he tried whistling, his parched lips could produce no sound.

As was usual with him in the evenings, he was wearing plimsolls, but he had just decided against running when events proved it to be un-necessary anyway: Bruno found a ginger cat and had soon given himself the satisfaction of chasing it up a tree. It was while Bruno was waking the nightly echoes with his excitement about this that Mr. Goodenough of the off-licence, who owned the ginger cat, came out of his side door and angrily announced their relationship, while Mr. Prone was repairing the strap with a knot.

'That's my cat,' said Mr. Goodenough, 'and you'd better take that damned dog away.'

A normal Mr. Prone would have shrugged and taken Bruno away, but this was not the normal Mr. Prone; it was one who not only disliked Mr. Goodenough but had had such a day as might reasonably nourish a dislike of the entire human species.

'I don't know', said Mr. Prone a little breathlessly, 'which is the big-ger damn nuisance, my dog chasing your ginger cat up a tree, where it can't do any harm for a while, or your ginger cat scratching up my garden, just because your own garden is smothered in weeds.'

'What do you mean, smothered in weeds?'

'There isn't a square foot of soil in your garden for a cat to use', Mr. Prone explained. 'So what does it do? Comes and uses mine. And as for weeds—'

'As for weeds,' retorted Mr. Goodenough, 'you've got more to the square inch in your garden than I've got to the square yard, you've got thistle and ragwort and I don't know what, and you ought to do some-thing about them. . . . Oh, just look at that dog now! Take the disgust-ing thing away from here *please*. Can't you read simple notices about dogs fouling the pavements?'

There were indeed plenty of these, on local authority installations of all kinds ranging from lamp standards to refuse bins. But whereas Mr. Prone had often read them, Bruno had not; and Bruno at that moment was earnestly fouling the pavement, without having given his master one moment in which to assume the air of studied disengagement of the dog-owner taken by surprise.

'That's just about all it needed', said Mr. Goodenough. 'That's just a bit more than I'm going to take. I'm going to complain about this.'

Mr. Prone contemplated the bit that his neighbour was proposing not to take.

'That's not on the pavement', he said.

'That certainly is on the pavement.'

'Kerbstone', said Mr. Prone.

They both glared at the ground.

'I don't call that kerbstone just there', Mr. Goodenough decided grimly.

'Half and half perhaps. I'd had to shorten the lead, you see?'

'Anyway what the law says is footway', Mr. Goodenough snapped. 'That's on the footway, that is. Footway includes kerbstone. And I'm glad it was you that said kerbstone, because now at least you can't deny it's there or that your dog did it.'

'It's only the excitement', said Mr. Prone, now very slightly ingratiating, 'about the cat.'

'Perhaps you will notice that's one thing cats *never* do', said Mr. Goodenough, who had no dog. 'Cats never foul the footway. They keep to gardens.'

'Other people's', said Mr. Prone. 'Goodnight.'

Back home, Bruno settled down now with surprising indifference to the Jack Russells, but these barked all night. Three sleepless neighbours telephoned in the small hours, and in the life of a retail newsagent those are very small indeed; and two others rang the side-door bell. Each time it was Mr. Prone, with an overcoat over his pyjamas, who went out to the dogs hoping to cajole, persuade, pacify, or intimidate them into silence and possibly sleep. Eventually at half-past four he got them each an enormous meal, the consumption of which helped to convince them that this might turn out, after all, to be not such a bad place as it looked, and was followed by an uneasy and half-contented respite. But by that time it was five o'clock and the morning paper vans were arriving.

Thursday

MR. PRONE came into the bedroom bearing the cup of tea by means of which, morning after morning, he tacitly retained ultimate command of the household.

'As soon as this mild weather's over those dogs will have to be brought indoors', he said. 'Where? Have you thought of that?'

'No they won't', said Mrs. Prone after two grateful sips, the first of which always cleared a channel so that the second, and those that followed, went down without touching the sides. 'Jimmy and some of his friends are going to build them a shed, proper windows and everything.'

'Shed? Who's talking about building sheds? You remember the trouble Lucas had over his shed?'

'That was a laboratory, for chemical work and things. We're not chemists. Of course I remember it. We don't need a thing *that* size. No bigger than a small garage.'

'We'd have to ask the Town Hall about it, anyway, the Town Planning people.'

'*They* wouldn't be interested, not in a little shed like this', she said scornfully. But she was forgetting the man she had married, the desperate role for which Fate and the Laws of England had now selected him, and the capacity of officials to officiate. It is of course anticipating events to reveal here that planning permission for the dogs' shed was peremptorily refused, but this part of the Prone story may as well be cleared up without delay. Once again Mr. Prone took his grievance to Mr. Parrott the solicitor.

'My advice to you is not to build it', said Mr. Parrott. 'Yes, you could chance it and hope it would never be noticed; lots of people do. But if it is noticed, you can be ordered to take it all down again. I happen to know that our Planning Committee turns everything down first time round, so that anyone who *really* wants planning permission has to be mad keen enough to appeal against them and get an inquiry. The first application, with all the form-filling and drawings and waiting for a hearing—that's only like knocking on the door or ringing the bell. Opens the way to the Appeals Committee, that's the only body that ever says yes.'

'Thank you', Mr. Prone said bitterly. 'That's your advice. Now tell me what you would *do* if it was yourself, and your wife wanted to breed dogs.'

'I'd talk her out of the dogs. Or if I couldn't do that, they'd have to sleep indoors somewhere. I wouldn't build them an outhouse.'

But as it turned out, Mr. Prone did not further pursue his planning application and the shed never got built, for adequate reasons which will appear.

The morning's routine was developing until it became apparent that Susan had no intention of getting up. Why, demanded Mr. Prone, was this?

It turned out that the day before, and the day before that, she had been sent home because she was wearing jeans; and that this was the culmination of a long feud about which Mr. Prone had been allowed by his womenfolk to know little or nothing. Mr. Hobbs, the headmaster, whose pupils were of both sexes and still tended to look like it, was against jeans for the girls. Mrs. Prone was against Mr. Hobbs, the headmaster. Susan was against being ordered home for wearing perfectly modest and conventional clothing which she felt happy in.

'Why wasn't I told about this?' demanded Mr. Prone.

His wife said she thought he had more than enough to worry about already. He had been so busy on Tuesday and Wednesday, and away from the shop so much, that there had been no difficulty about concealing Susan's presence during what should have been her school hours. She had been useful in the shop at times, she had been doing her school work at others. Mrs. Prone was going to tell him about it that morning, for she was not going to have that Mr. Hobbs dictating to *her* what Susan was to wear. But now he knew about it anyway; and Susan wasn't going to school.

'You mean to say,' said Mr. Prone, in words so predictable that she could have scribbled them out for him, 'that in the middle of getting ready for her exams she's throwing all her chances away just because of these damned trousers?'

He disapproved of trousers for women anyway because, he had been heard to say far too often, from behind they looked like a departing elephant. But he disapproved much more of arbitrary behaviour by schoolmasters or schoolmistresses; and Susan, he ordained, was to get up at once and go to school—whether she wore jeans or not. If she had now left it too late to have any breakfast, that was her fault. While she was dressing he would write her a note she could hand to the headmaster. It would be about jeans.

Dear Mr. Hobbs [said the note]
I do not understand why you have sent my daughter Susan Prone home from school for wearing jeans, they are a very suitable kind of wear for a girl nowadays and her mother wears them too. My daughter is in the middle of studying for her O Level exams and it is not right that her studies should be broken into like this, I hope we shall hear no more of this nonsense.
                                            Yours truly,
                                                P. Prone

Then he crossed out 'nonsense' and sat trying to think of a substitute that might in some way be stronger and yet less offensive. Failing in which, he wrote 'nonsense' again, sealed the envelope and gave it to Susan, who took it unwillingly and hurried off to school with her mouth full of toast.

'Sandra Lucas is at home for wearing eye-shadow', said Mrs. Prone. 'She's about fifteen too and wants to do O-levels. The thing is, neither of them can be enrolled for the exam if they're not at school next month when it's done. She pinches eye-shadow from her father's shop, and that headmaster, he just won't have it. I think he's a bit of a crank, all the parents think so.'

Mr. Prone nodded. 'Well, we shall see. I think that's a police helmet going past the window. No, it's not going past, it's coming in. Oh God, no, it's Flynn.'

Police Constable Flynn nodded as he closed the shop door. 'Morning', he said in the tone of a man who expects no satisfactory response. 'Is that your notice board on the corner of Sandford Hill?'

'Notice board?' said a genuinely puzzled Mr. Prone. 'What are you talking about *now*?'

P.C. Flynn took out his notebook. ' "Jack Russell puppies for Sale",' he read out. ' "Ready January 30th. Spenser Park General Stores." Did you put that up?'

'I certainly did not. Put it up where?'

P.C. Flynn put his head on one side.

'No? Now I wonder who would be putting up something like that with your name on it, and you not knowing?'

Mrs. Prone then saw her husband turning slowly and incredulously towards her. 'It was Jimmy,' she said, 'first thing this morning.'

'What!' said Mr. Prone. 'Jimmy?'

'He wanted to make a notice board about the puppies, he's mad about them, he's been doing this board for two days—kept on spoiling it, he reckoned, and beginning again. Then he nailed it to an old clothes prop of mine and wanted to put it up on that piece of waste land at the top of Sandford Hill. I said we didn't know who the land belonged to, I didn't see where we went for permission but I would find out. And then he goes and puts it up this morning before school, him and young Alec Bond, he helped him make it and came round to help him put it up.'

During this recital Mr. Prone had been watching his wife in genuine astonishment, while P.C. Flynn was gratefully writing things in his little book.

'And no one asked permission before erecting this advertisement board?' said the policeman without looking up.

'Whose permission?' asked Mr. Prone. 'It's waste land, isn't it?'

'The owner of the land, for one thing; and the Town Planning Committee, for another—the Town Hall.'

'I didn't know anything about it,' Mr. Prone said, 'but I'm going to take that thing down, now that I do know.'

P.C. Flynn wrote something else in his little book.

'That ought to make a difference in the magistrate's mind', he said soothingly. 'Breeding dogs, are you?' he went on before Mr. Prone could take up the question of magistrates' minds.

'That's my wife's affair, not mine.'

'Well, I expect you'll be getting a call from the local authority vet, so I won't bother you any more about that myself. Could you let me see one of your billheads, printed stationery?'

'What for? This is all we use', said Mrs. Prone innocently, and she handed him a sheet of notepaper headed 'Spenser Park General Stores'.

He looked at it carefully. 'It came into my mind,' he said, 'while I was looking at the notice board about the puppies. Yes, you see I'm afraid this doesn't conform to the law.'

'What law?' said Mr. Prone incredulously. 'What have you dug up now?'

'There's a law about people trading under made-up names like this.'

'Against me calling myself a General Stores?'

'I didn't say *against*, did I? I said about.'

'Are you trying to say we can't call ourselves the Spenser Park General Stores? Who's complaining, the park authorities?'

'Oh no no. You mustn't trade in a made-up name without publishing your true name as well.'

'Look, that's our name, that is, not a made-up name. Or anyway we didn't make it up.'

'You weren't christened Spenser Park General Stores? What's on your birth certificate?'

'You just couldn't be funny if you took lessons. My name is Percival Prone and you know it is.'

'Then that's what ought to be on your billheads and business letters somewhere, whatever else might be there. No, I forget the name of the Act[1] for the moment, but the penalty's £5. And you have to be registered with the Registrar of Business Names, that's another penalty of £5 a day for as long as you've been doing it.'

'Doing what?'

'Failing to register.'

'Good God, that goes back—what—ten years or more, ever since we've been here? £5 a day for all that time? That would only be about twenty thousand quid or something.'

---

[1] Registration of Business Names Act 1916, section 1(b): 'Every individual carrying on business under a business name which does not consist of his true surname without any additions other than his true Christian names or the initials thereof' shall be registered in manner provided by this Act; and 'shall, in all trade catalogues, trade circulars, showcards and business letters on which the business name appears ... have mentioned in legible characters his present Christian name or the initials thereof and present surname' (section 18).

'It's what they call a continuing offence, you see, but I can't tell you when the penalty would start from. They may decide it's from the day I report the offence, or from the day you started business here.'

'Couldn't it possibly start from the day the previous chap started business here? That would take you back to about 1909, wouldn't that be nice? Anyway who are "they"? And how would they set about proving what was happening before *you* came trunking in?'

'It's the Department of Trade, and you're probably right', said the unruffled Flynn. 'Still, we shall have to see, won't we?'

And P.C. Flynn made another of his all-too-brief exits from the lives of the Prones.

It wasn't long, however, before they were confronted by a veterinary officer from the Town Hall. Once this latest intruder had announced himself and introduced the subject of dog-breeding, Mr. Prone's bitterness was intense.

'Didn't take you long to get off the mark then, did it?' he said. 'You and that Flynn work together, do you? Everyone dances to that man's tune, but you certainly haven't lost any time.'

'Flynn? I never heard of him. What do you mean, Mr. Prone?'

'I mean he's out to ruin me, that's what', shouted Mr. Prone. 'And it was him that came and told you about those dogs, he's only just been here about them.'

'On the contrary, it was a Mr. and Mrs. Darling, they're dog-breeders registered with us under the Breeding of Dogs Act 1973. They kept three Jack Russell bitches. They notified us last week that they were giving up their licence and wanted it transferred to you. Well, a licence can't be transferred from one breeder to another because it relates to their own premises; but I gather you have acquired their animals?'

So that was it. He fumed. If his wife didn't know about licences for dog-breeding, why hadn't she found out? It was none of his doing.

Mrs. Prone too was indignant.

'Licence?' she said. 'Transferred to us? I haven't had time yet to get a dog licence for them—'

'Three dog licences. You'll need a licence for each.'

'Eh? Well, three then. Anyway I *thought* they were not transferable, so that's no news.'

'But you see I'm not talking about dog licences, I mean a licence for a dog-breeding establishment.'

'Establishment?' spluttered Mr. Prone. 'This isn't a zoo. I'm not having this turned into any kind of establishment. This is just another part of the whole damn silly conspiracy—'

'What's in a word, Mr. Prone? Let me tell you just how the Act of Parliament defines a breeding establishment, shall I? Here it is: "Breeding establishment means any premises (including a private dwelling) where more than two bitches are kept for the purpose of breeding for sale." I gather you've got the three?'

'There's only one in whelp', said Mrs. Prone defensively.

'Half a minute', Mr. Prone said suddenly. He had been looking thoughtful. 'What happens if we get rid of one bitch? Then we've only got two?'

'Then you wouldn't need a breeder's licence, of course.'

'Right. That's it, then. One of them goes today.'

'Oh now listen, Percy—'

'I mean what I say. I didn't ask for all this dog business anyway, you sprang it on me.'

'I'm not getting rid of any of those Jack Russells, whatever you say.'

The veterinary officer coughed. 'You might be interested', he said, 'to hear what the licensing conditions are, I've got them here. We should have to ensure that you kept the dogs in suitable accommodation—and that means construction and size of quarters, the number of dogs in them, exercising facilities, temperature, lighting, ventilation, and cleanliness. They'd have to be "adequately supplied with *suitable* food, drink and bedding material, adequately exercised, and visited at suitable intervals". And you'd have to take reasonable precautions to prevent the spread of diseases among the dogs, and to protect them against fire and other emergencies (that includes flood). And of course we should have to supervise what was going on, how you were complying with all this—'

'I've heard about enough', said Mr. Prone. 'Thank you for calling. Those dogs are for sale, and they're not going to stay here while someone makes up their mind to buy them, either.'

Mrs. Prone was silent.

'Those dogs are for sale,' said Mr. Prone again, 'and we're not keeping them here—'

'All right, I heard', she said sadly. 'All right.' She swallowed. 'How do we sell them then, if we can't do it here?'

'The Excelsior Kennels will sell them for you', said the vet. 'Only don't say I gave you their name. They're very reliable. They'll sell them and take a commission. I can't think why the previous owners didn't take them there, if they really are decent Jack Russells.'

'Mrs. Darling wanted to know they were going to a good home', said Mrs. Prone complacently.

'Where they'd sleep out in the back yard,' said Mr. Prone, 'coming up to Christmas. Look,' he said to the vet, 'could you perhaps have a look at them and tell me what they're worth?'

'I don't know about that, but I ought to have a look at them anyway.' And the veterinary inspector was conducted into the back yard, where stood the three kennels and prowled the three dogs.

'Well,' he said at once, 'you can't keep them out here, can you? Much too cold. Better get rid of them anyway if you can't have them indoors.' He briefly examined each animal.

'They might be worth about £30 each, I suppose,' he said, 'but that's quite unofficial and I shall deny having said it.'

When he had gone, Mr. Prone hurried along to the corner of Sandford Hill and took down the notice about the dogs. Within an hour they were available for purchase at the Excelsior Kennels, and another Prone episode was nearly closed. What may be said to have closed it more happily than former episodes was the subsequent sale of the Jack Russells for £80.

As soon as he got back to the shop, of course, he saw that the next episode was beginning. This much was apparent from the presence of Mrs. Prendergast, the lady who spoke without breathing or punctuation because they wasted time.

'I'm not one to complain', she was saying as he came in, and it was plain that this was a partial replay for his special benefit, 'but the law's got to be the same for everyone hasn't it I don't see why they should stop me saying "Youth wanted for garden work" I mean if I wanted a girl I would say girl wouldn't I?'

'What's all this about?' was Mr. Prone's none too friendly greeting. And as Mrs. Prone turned from serving a customer, her facial expression changed from business charm to concentrated ferocity, a smile disappearing like a smear of butter on a hot stove.

'Mrs. Prendergast says my advert in the window is illegal', she told her husband in a voice that was only just under control.

'What advert? Who's put an advertisement in our window then?'

'Oh I did, yesterday. I told you I need another girl in the shop, didn't I? We *can't* have Susan seen working here on schooldays, just because of this no-jeans business, or they'll think there's more in it than the jeans. And as I say she's supposed to be working for O-levels.'

'I see. So you put an advert in the window. Saying what?'

'That's just it,' said Mrs. Prendergast, 'I saw it yesterday and I thought good gracious and I asked my husband and he said if we can't do it neither can they he said it's the Racial Equals Act or something he called it—'

'Do you MIND?' snapped Mrs. Prone. 'I've heard at the Towns-women's Guild there are a lot of unemployed West Indian girls in the district and people say they're very good workers and they ask less money.'

'Less than who? Less than men or less than white girls?' demanded her husband.

'Less than either. And you can't get a white girl, or a man either, for this kind of job anyway, at what we can afford to pay.'

'And what I say is if you ask me', took up Mrs. Prendergast though no one had, 'that you mustn't advertise for anybody who is male or female and you mustn't advertise for anybody who isn't black or Negro or Indian or something or anybody who *is* black or Negro and all that—'

'I didn't know you'd advertised at all', growled Mr. Prone. 'Let's get this straight. The law says we mustn't ask for a girl, mustn't ask for a boy, mustn't ask for a black man, mustn't ask for a white man, mustn't ask for an Irishman, a Spaniard, an Italian or anything. What *can* we ask for, some sort of a colourless bloke who comes from nowhere'—there came a sudden rush of words—'some sort of a stateless eunuch who isn't any colour at all?'

'What I say is if you ask me', said Mrs. Prendergast, though again this was not what Mr. Prone had been doing, 'is what's fair for one is fair for all my husband says if you can go on selling cigarettes to children and letting your wretched dog get at our chickens and breaking the law left right and centre and all the things you've been getting up to Mr. Prone yes I know all about it you're the talk of the neighbourhood well then it's time some of us tried to help the authorities a bit and if you don't take that advertisement out of your window I shall have to tell them at the Labour Exchange I mean there's enough trouble about coloured people round here as it is—'

'DO YOU MIND?' shrieked Mrs. Prone, and her husband, opening the door, indicated with a sweep of his arm that this was the moment for Mrs. Prendergast to go. Encouraged by something in their joint demeanour, she went.

'I must ask Mr. Parrott about all this', he said. 'I've got a lot to talk to him about this evening. Where is it all going to end?'

Mrs. Prone ventured no prophecy. Instead she filled in a little more information about the visit of Mrs. Prendergast.

'She didn't really come about that advertisement', said Mrs. Prone gently. 'She just noticed it on the way in.'

'Oh?'

'She brought in this packet of Edwards's Sponge Trifle. She bought it here yesterday and it's got a date on it—"Sell by 10 September".'

'What? Who sold it to her?'

'I did. Never looked at the date. Well, we got it from Dellows' with the last order, there's lots of them still left. I expect they're all 10 September. They usually sell quickly at this time of the year.'

'I bet they're perfectly all right. They're all sugar, those things, keep for years.'

'They don't, Percy. This one didn't.'

'What? Let me look at it then.'

'She took it away with her. Said she and her wretched husband are going to take legal advice about it.'

'Are they, by God? So am I then. Another one for Mr. Parrott.'

Mr. Prone was just sitting down to his midday meal when Susan came home again. 'Mr. Hobbs said to give you this note', she said.

Dear Mr. Prone,

Susan has been told repeatedly by her form mistress that she must not wear jeans to school. It is a rule that applies to all the girls, and is accepted by everyone without trouble. I do not happen to see why Susan should be the one exception; and if this were allowed, it would be difficult to enforce other rules without permitting illogical exceptions. I presume that you have taken advice about what you are doing, but so have I. She must not return to school unless she wears a skirt or dress. Meanwhile her education is the victim of your own obstinacy.

Yours truly,

J. R. HOBBS

'Why, I never did come across anything so ridiculous', was Mrs. Prone's reaction to this exercise in tact and diplomacy. 'The man must be mad!'

'I'm not so sure', Mr. Prone said unexpectedly. 'I think he's got a point.'

'WHAT! He's entitled to say how my child shall be dressed?'

'Well, maybe. Quite a lot of people can tell us how to dress. The police take a bit of interest now and again. And the magistrates do, too—and some kinds of employers. It's all very well to stand up for your rights and all that, but who says they're rights? Never any harm in changing your mind. Nothing wrong with jeans, of course, but suppose that school had no rules at all? He'd have some of them turning up in ponchos, some in bare feet. In the hot weather there'd be some in bathing trunks or bikinis, some in nothing at all I shouldn't wonder.'

'Daddy, you can change your mind as often as you like,' said Susan, 'but I'm not changing my jeans.'

Mr. Prone contemplated his daughter with surprise but not with total disapproval. How (he was asking himself) does a man make a fifteen-year-old daughter conform to a school regulation if the school itself can't do it? What sanctions can he apply? He could withhold her pocket-money, of course, but Susan frequently and quite willingly helped in the shop, with access to the till; and if she took from the till no more than what he had usually given her on Saturday mornings, would that be stealing?[1] The result of this cogitation, when it found expression, was not impressive.

'Then what', said Mr. Prone, 'are you reckoning to do about your O-level exams?'

'The girls all say I can study at home and turn up in my jeans for the exams and then he can't send me home, and that's what I'm going to do.'

'But the exams aren't for another six months, you can't sit at home here for six months when you're supposed to be at school.'

'I'm sixteen on the 9th February,' said Susan pertly, 'and I can leave then anyway. Then I can help in the shop part-time, and set my own homework, and get ready for the exam without all that rot about "mock O-levels". There's lots of important people never went to school at all. Bertrand Russell never did, he went to University but he never went to school.'

Mr. Prone glared at her. 'If you think you're a female Bertrand Russell,' he said tartly, 'you can tell that to the education man when he calls—because call he will.'

And on that very day, call he did. 'Mr. Prone?' he said. 'Yes. You have a daughter Susan who is a registered pupil at Gresham Road Secondary Modern School, and she is not attending school regularly within the meaning of section 39 of the Education Act 1944.'

Succinctly, Mr. Prone told him why. 'So what?' added Mr. Prone.

'She is under the age of sixteen, I believe?'

'She's sixteen on 9th February.'

'So she is of compulsory school age, and', said the inspector like a man reciting, 'she is not receiving efficient full-time education suitable to her age, ability, and aptitude.'

---

[1] Not, Mr. Parrott informed him later, if she did it 'in the belief that she had in law the right to deprive him of it' (Theft Act 1968, section 2(a)). And that was precisely the kind of belief she would have

'Who says she isn't?' said Mr. Prone with sudden belligerence. 'Are you making out that school is the only place where she can get that?'

'Not at all, I—'

'Because there's plenty of children get good education at home without going to school, always did, and if there's going to be much of this nonsense I shall get Mrs. Lucas to coach her, she was a headmistress.'

'Mrs. Lucas?' said the education officer, who seemed unshaken by this.

'The chemist's wife, next door but one.'

'Ah yes, I have to call there too. Sandra Lucas is the daughter there, is she? Yes, I see. She's also at home because of a dispute.'

'Eye-shadow', said Mrs. Prone. 'Lot of stupid rot, I call it. Anyway these two girls can quite well be coached for O-levels by Mrs. Lucas, and I'm sure she'll be willing to do it, Percy—we can arrange about a fee.'

'I see', said the education officer. 'Well, that's something we must look at, isn't it?'

Mrs. Prone, fresh from the counting of puppies before they were whelped, was even now recklessly counting chickens before they were hatched. She found that Mrs. Lucas was by no means interested in coaching their respective daughters for O-level exams. It turned out that if there was one thing more exasperating to Mrs. Lucas than the appearance of eye-shadow on schoolgirls, it was the use of eye-shadow stolen by her own daughter from her husband's pharmacy. A great row was in intermittent progress at the Lucases, and it was going to end in Sandra's return to school with normal eyelids. Did the Prones realize, asked Mrs. Lucas that evening, what they were doing? If Susan was not enrolled at the school for the forthcoming O-level examinations—and this must be done in January—she could only take them as a student at some external examination centre, some village hall or somewhere, on payment of the £5 fee which the school would normally be paying for her.

'And I could wear my jeans?' said Susan.

'So far as I know you could go as a Bunny girl. But of course if you were found too much of a distraction you could be classed as a nuisance and turned out. And serve you right, my girl.'

'I class her as a nuisance now', said Mr. Prone. 'Susan, you're going to school tomorrow in a skirt or a dress, and you are going to stop playing the fool. Until these exams are over there won't be any more serving in the shop—'

'Oh but, look here Daddy, what do I do for pocket money?'

'We'll work out something about that', her father said, thinking about the £80 windfall from the Jack Russells. 'And I have redone the window advertisement for a new assistant, something specially for the Race Relations man to read. Get an eyeful of this', and he produced a large white envelope on which he had carefully printed the following in block capitals:

RACE RELATIONS ACT
SEX DISCRIMINATION ACT
EQUAL OPPORTUNITIES ACT
ASSISTANT REQUIRED
To serve in shop. Male, female, or mixed. Black, white, brown, pink, violet, indigo, blue, green, yellow, orange, red. Must understand some English, walk upright, know what day it is, and answer to some sort of name. Apply within.

'Worked it out with old Lucas', said Mr. Prone. 'You wait till Mrs. Prendergast sees it', he added, with the nearest approach to a smile since he had seen Mr. Whiffen fall off a ladder the previous Friday.

The ever-available Mr. Parrott offered no resistance when the Prones asked if they could drive round to see him that evening. Indeed he now welcomed each Prone instalment as an improvement on anything offered by television in the evenings; it was a this-is-bigger-than-either-of-us phenomenon. In the normal way he was a bit tired of practising as a solicitor and sleeping on the same premises, 'living over the shop'; but it had its advantages, and the Prones were now among them.

'You'd taken me as far as the Jack Russells', he said, pouring them each what seemed to Mr. Prone a rather big glass of sherry.

They told him of the mollifying sequel and, when he had rejoiced with them, passed on to the question of Susan's jeans.

'Ah, jeans', he said, almost as if they had said hashish or LSD. 'Of course if you wanted to contest the headmaster's decision, you might do it by way of an application in the Queen's Bench Division to have it declared *ultra vires*.'

'Ultra what?'

'Beyond the headmaster's powers. Sometimes the judges will hold that a particular rule laid down by someone who has the power to make rules is contrary to natural justice and goes beyond what he ought to do.'

'How long would it take to get to the High Court with that?'

'About two years, I should think, at present rates of progress. Not much good, eh? The other way round is to wait till you get a magistrate's summons for not sending Susan to school, as you probably will, and then we can defend on the ground that this no-jeans business is a needlessly oppressive rule. If that fails, and you're convicted (and whether you appeal or not), you can still apply to the Examining Board for Susan to be allowed to take her exams at an external examination centre, I mean away from the school. That would cost you about a fiver *but* you would need the consent of the headmaster as well as the Examining Board's.'

'What! He simply wouldn't give it.'

'Oh, I should think he probably would. But of course if he didn't, well then, she couldn't take her O-level exams, could she?'

'Are you telling me that a girl can be denied the right to take exams because of what she's got on her legs?'

'I wouldn't have thought of it that way, but yes, that's quite a neat way of putting it. Funny, isn't it, how important clothes can still be?'

Nothing had ever seemed less funny to Mr. Prone. He had already made his grudging decision about what was to go on Susan's legs, but he still wanted to know what was to happen if she now defied him as well as the school. He couldn't, he pleaded, tie her up and drive her to school as a captive. Or, if he did, ensure that she stayed there once she had been delivered. What *would* happen? Would they come and take her away somewhere, some approved school or something? If they did, she wouldn't stay there either. She'd run away and keep on running away.

'You've become a real bitter-ender, haven't you?' said Mr. Parrott. He generously refilled the sherry glasses; and from his Mr. Prone took a large nervous gulp. 'Well, we don't have approved schools any more, they're called community homes. If you ask me I don't think there would be all that much fuss about a girl who is sixteen in February anyway, a couple of months to go. But of course I suppose you know that in the educational world there's a special way of "attaining" a particular age, and it's got nothing much to do with birthdays. Susan has to attend school until she has "attained the age of sixteen years", but under the Education Act that has a meaning you might not expect. In her case, as her sixteenth birthday comes between the beginning of February and the end of the summer term, she's got to go to school until the Friday before the last Monday in May.[1] No two ways about that. But I suppose the Department of Education and Science might send you a summons; the first hearing would be fixed for about the end of January, then there'd be an adjournment, then the court would hear to its pretended surprise

[1] Education Act 1962, section 9, as amended by the Education (School Leaving Dates) Act 1976, section 1.

that Susan was now sixteen; and then in the present state of court
business the whole thing might well get lost. So that would really be the
end of it, though nobody would admit it was. And you might be ordered
to pay the costs.'

'That's it—I thought there was going to be a catch in this. And what
could the costs be?'

'Difficult to say. £25 perhaps. More than the whole thing is worth.
Any use *my* seeing Susan, do you think, having a talk with her?'

'None at all', said Mr. Prone ungratefully, and passed on to the subject of Jimmy's do-it-yourself notice board concerning the Jack Russells.

'That', said Mr. Parrott, 'is one of these neighbourhood problems
where the State has stepped in and taken a hand. It's something called
the Town and Country Planning (Control of Advertisements) Regulations, and it means you can't put up notice boards and hoardings without permission from the local authority.'

'I don't say anything about that,' rejoined Mr. Prone, 'but there's a
notice board on that bit of ground near the park, it's always there, permanent, and just now it says "Logs, 200 yards" but in the summer it'll
say "Strawberries—200 yards". And do you know who puts it there?
Them gipsies. Are you telling me the Town Hall gives *them* a licence
for it? Because if so—'

'No no, most unlikely. If someone complained about it, then you'd
soon find it was removed. Why don't you complain?'

'Me? I'm not complaining about it, Mr. Parrott. Anyway is that how
the law really works? Nothing happens if no one complains? Because if
that's right, what was Flynn getting on to me for?'

'Oh, he *may* have received a complaint. A policeman of that kind
attracts complaints the way a dustbin attracts flies. But there doesn't
have to be a complaint about advertisement hoardings, from anyone
saying they're annoyed or obstructed or something. An unauthorized
notice board in a public place is just a breach of the planning laws, all
the complaining's been done in the past. But even if you didn't think
your little board was a blot on the landscape, what would you think if
someone came and put up a board on the forecourt in front of your
shop?'

'Oh, well, that forecourt's part of my property.'

'Mr. Prone, when will you ever learn? That forecourt is public footway, public highway. That's why you're in trouble about your news-
stand outside the shop.'

'All right, well, I'd like to see anyone try putting up a notice board
on it anyway.'

The lesson seemed to have gone home.

'I don't suppose you'll hear any more about it', Mr. Parrott said. 'The thing was put up without your knowledge and taken down the moment you knew about it. The actual offender was Jimmy and he's how old?'

'Ten in January.'

'Then he's below the age of criminal responsibility. He can't commit any crime or any offence of any sort.'[1]

Unexpectedly Mr. Prone felt—and looked—as though a significant prop had been removed from his authority in the home. His own father had often threatened, when he was a boy, to 'send for a policeman' (though he never did) as a sequel to some crime of no greater moment than the unauthorized consumption of sugar lumps or jam. And with an indelible recollection of its temporary effect on moral boundaries, he himself had kept it in reserve for Jimmy. And now it was no use?

'So my boy', said Mr. Prone, 'can do what he likes and the law doesn't want to know?' He was speaking with the bitterness of a man of whose affairs the law had for the past week seemed bent on knowing far too much.

'Oh but it does', Mr. Parrott assured him as he once more replenished the sherry glasses. 'It might come to regard him as "exposed to moral danger", or beyond your control.[2] And then the magistrates could require you to take proper care of Jimmy, exercise proper control over him, or they could put him under the supervision of the local child care officer or a probation officer. Or they could make a "care order" sending him to a community home.'

'Over my dead body', explained Mrs. Prone briefly. 'Anyway, there's no question of that and we're wasting Mr. Parrott's time. We wanted to ask him about that Edwards's Sponge Trifle and the Prendergasts.'

They moved on to the question of the sponge trifle.

'Powdered or something, is it?' said Mr. Parrott.

'Dehydrated', Mr. Prone said. 'You add water and heat it up, and then you wait till it gets cold again.'

'Sounds absolutely lousy to me. What kind of a sponge trifle could grow out of that? Still, people are certainly swallowing some very odd things these days. What did the label say—"Sell by 10 September"? Well, as it happens I can tell you something about this date-labelling business. It *doesn't* mean "must be eaten by" 10 September. I've been involved in one or two of these cases lately. The dates on perishable goods are only very broad guides. I'm told they allow a wide

---

[1] Children and Young Persons Act 1933, section 50, as amended in 1963. 'It shall be conclusively presumed that no child under the age of 10 years can be guilty of any offence.'

[2] Children and Young Persons Act 1969, section 1.

margin of safety, and they don't mean that some awful kind of putrefaction sets in on 11 September. More sherry?'

'Not for my husband', said Mrs. Prone quickly, protectively, and anxiously. 'He's not really used to very much.'

Mr. Parrott (and, for that matter, a slightly shamefaced Mr. Prone) accepted the implication that she was different.

'The fact is,' went on Mr. Parrott, 'a lot of perishable food is being wasted because of this date-marking business. They're trying to work out a more sensible code of practice, based on scientific research into what they call the life-span of perishable foods. But anyway the date-stamping we've got at the moment certainly comes down on the side of safety. Mrs. Prendergast didn't say she'd seen any green mould or anything?'

'Nothing, no.'

'Or any maggots?'

'This is simply disgusting', said Mrs. Prone feelingly. 'No one else has complained about that consignment, and we've eaten several of those things ourselves?'

'Fine', Mr. Parrott said. 'Then I think you can take it you won't hear any more. After all, *de minimis non curat lex*.'

'I beg your pardon', said Mr. Prone.

'The law takes no account of Trifles', said Mr. Parrott, whose gratification at his own little joke then became totally uncontrollable. As he rolled about and obviously expected them to do the same, Mr. Prone watched with growing distaste the heaving of his shoulders and the tears oozing out on to his cheeks.

'I think it's time we went', Mr. Prone said, getting up. 'Thank you very much, Mr. Parrott, for all your help.'

'I think that's a police car behind', said Mrs. Prone. She had been waving goodbye to Mr. Parrott as he stood at the top of the flaking stone steps by which you approached his front door. Mr. Prone glanced in his mirror.

'I can't see anything at all behind', he said.

But this was because the police car was at that moment overtaking him, and a moment later it was in front and 'waving him down'.

'Another minute and you'd have been gone', said a young policeman who then emerged from it. 'Towed away. Don't you know this road is closed for parking?'

'Closed for parking? I've parked there a good many times lately, that's my solicitor's house', said Mr. Prone, with an immediate sense of pre-emptive one-upmanship.

'Do you know what a traffic cone is? You knocked one over as you drove away just now.'

'Traffic cone? You mean that tin can thing? That was lying down already, those things are always lying down. Are they yours? What are they for?'

'You don't even know what they're for? Do you notice they've got "Metropolitan Police" on them? Does that give you any ideas? Look, we've got this road restricted this evening because of the Queen's visit to the new Town Hall. So there are traffic cones all the way along. You didn't see any of them when you parked your car? You've been there two hours.'

'Nobody told me about the Queen', said Mr. Prone, and nobody had. He was in favour of kings and queens, especially queens, but his life had lately been too full for him to notice what the Queen was doing with hers. 'I didn't see any traffic cones, no. And I'll tell you something else,' he went on, raising his voice and unconsciously doing it for a large number of his fellow citizens, 'I wouldn't have known what they meant if I did see them and I bet the Queen doesn't know either, or care.'

The policeman had now been joined by another one. They both seemed to be finding him specially interesting, obviously thinking about him in the rather primitive way that marks the policeman who doesn't quite know what he is thinking. Suddenly one of them stepped very close to him, so close that their noses nearly touched, and said he would like to see his driving licence.

Mr. Prone breathed heavily.

'Ah!' he said. 'Now that's a thing I can't help you with at this very moment.' He was on the point of saying that he had applied for a renewal and that his fresh licence was probably in the post to him. He changed his mind strategically and said (more wisely): 'Actually I haven't got it with me at the moment.'

But whichever of these remarks he had uttered, what mattered was that the breath on which those remarks must be borne was carried straight to the policeman's nostrils, which found them to reek of alcohol.

'That's all right, we can see it later on—within five days at the police station. What I really want you to do is to blow hard into this little bag.' And the constable produced a breathalyser bag and held it up before Mr. Prone's astonished and indignant gaze.

'Are you suggesting that I'm drunk?' he asked, with what was intended to be a convincing show of outraged abstemiousness. And he could not know how difficult it is for better actors than he to breathe new life into a protest already made stale by 100,000 repetitions.

'Not me', said the policeman. 'If that suggestion comes from any-where, I reckon it'll come from this little bag. Now just take a deep breath and give it a long steady blow.'

'I shall do no such thing. You are simply playing the same game as all the others, I don't know who began it all—'

'I don't really know what you mean, sir, but I reckon I'd better tell you that if you refuse to give me a breath specimen I shall have to arrest you and take you to the station. And you *might* be convicted for refusing —it's an offence to refuse—and that would mean a fine, or perhaps prison, and disqualification.'

Mr. Prone glared at him. 'So I get arrested either way?' he said. 'You'll arrest me if I refuse and you'll arrest me if I don't refuse—'

'Half a minute', said the constable. 'What's that? I didn't say I'd arrest you either way. I can't arrest you if this breath sample is negative. That means if you've got less than 80 milligrammes of alcohol in every 100 millilitres of your blood.'

'But you reckon I've got more?'

'Well, I wouldn't be all that surprised, sir.'

'And that's why you stopped me? What was wrong with the way I was driving?'

'I haven't said there was anything wrong with the way you were driv-ing. I stopped you because you were driving in a road officially closed for parking. And then I could smell you had been drinking. One long steady blow please?'

And when Mr. Prone at last complied, the crystals in the container, as if (it seemed to him) by magic or trickery, turned green. But it was chemistry rather than magic or trickery, the vital contribution to the mixture being Mr. Parrott's sherry.

'I'm arresting you', said the policeman, now sounding very formal indeed because he was reading from a little card, 'for driving a motor vehicle on a road having consumed alcohol in such a quantity that the proportion in your blood exceeds the prescribed limit. You don't have to say anything unless you want to, but anything you do say, I shall write it down and it may be given in evidence.'

So far from being able to say anything that could be written down, Mr. Prone was noiselessly opening and closing his jaws with the rhyth-mic motion peculiar to him at moments of stress.

'Do you drive, madam?' one of the policemen asked Mrs. Prone. 'Can you follow us to the station?'

'Well, I do,' she said, 'but I've had as much sherry as he has and I don't think I will. Not that I'd have thought it was enough to turn one of those things green.'

'Ah well. I'll get your husband into the patrol car and then I'll drive this one.'

And thus they set off, Mr. Prone thinking, now in a rather confused way, that the events of the day had probably been happening to somebody else, and that he had perceived them with such objective clarity that they had really seemed to be happening to him.

At the police station he was told he could have another breath test if he liked; but that in any case he would now be required to submit to a blood test or (an alternative he primly rejected) to supply a specimen of urine. There ensued a wait of half an hour for a doctor, who briskly extracted some of the Prone blood, handed it to the station officer, nodded amiably at everyone, and departed. The precious fluid was divided between two small phials, one for dispatch to the police laboratory for analysis and report, the other for Mr. Prone to bear away as (he supposed) some kind of memento for the mantelpiece. He would be notified in a few weeks, he was told, as to the analyst's findings.

'A few *what*?' said the incredulous Mr. Prone.

'They're very busy, and so are the courts. You're going to tell me, of course, that analysing a blood sample only takes a few minutes, but there are *thousands* of these samples waiting to be done, Mr. Prone, yours is only one in a very long queue. It might be as long as eight weeks.'

While Mr. Prone was digesting this alarming piece of information, Mrs. Prone was wondering how they were going to get home.

'How long does it take *now* for him to be fit to drive?' she said. 'I mean this evening?'

'Oh, that seems to differ with everyone. Couldn't say. Not just yet anyway.'

'What about me?' she said. 'I'm all right to drive. Anyway I feel all right.'

'So did I', said her husband. 'That's nothing to do with it.'

'But I suppose they could find out with that breathing bag?'

The policemen contemplated her with a new and disturbed interest. Was the use of the breathalyser a public service, free on request to any intending driver who was torn by doubt? The station officer was called upon to express a view; and, having tapped his teeth for some time with a pencil, expressed it.

'You wouldn't get anyone driving up to a police station for a test', he said, 'if there was any chance that they *were* over the limit. That really would be asking for it? But when somebody is actually in the nick, and hasn't been doing any driving, and wants to know if it's all right, like this lady, well then I don't see why we shouldn't oblige.'

They obliged, and Mrs. Prone was found fit to drive; a discovery greeted by Mr. Prone with hopelessly mixed feelings.

'Little did they know', she said as they set off for home, 'that this is the very first time I've even attempted to drive this thing'—there was a brief pause for some gear-crashing—'but while there's this bother about your driving licence, perhaps I'd better do all the driving, just for a while?'

Mr. Prone reluctantly supposed she had. And indeed once he was home again, a delayed feeling of shock took possession of him and he declared his intention of going straight to bed.

'I should think so too', she said. 'Where do you think I'm going? I'll just put the car away, and see the children are all right, and then I'll make a cup of tea and I'll be up.'

At that moment Jimmy called from his bedroom. 'That you, Mum?'

'Good gracious, are you still awake?' she said, and she hurried up the stairs to Jimmy's bedroom door. 'Do you know it's after eleven o'clock? What's the matter? Susan,' she called, 'are *you* asleep?'

There was no reply from Susan's bedroom.

'Susan's not there', said Jimmy. 'She's gone across to the Rose and Crown with Alec Fraser, they went about nine o'clock, after Morecambe and Wise.'

Mrs. Prone was shocked.

'*Susan* in the Rose and Crown? She was told to stay with you. Whatever's your Dad going to think, specially after all this?'

'Why Mum? After all what?'

'Oh never mind—I'll tell you later. You get back into bed, I'll have to tell Dad where she is. . . . Percy,' she called, 'you'd better go across to the Rose and Crown, Susan's in there with a boy.'

It took some little time to convince Mr. Prone that he could have a fifteen-year-old daughter who was to be found in a pub, at any time, with anyone, especially after eleven o'clock at night. But at length he reluctantly accepted a father's duty to investigate. His mind had by this time recovered from Mr. Parrott's hospitality, and he peered out of the shop window at the Rose and Crown on the opposite corner.

'They've still got the lights on in the saloon bar', he said. 'Wonder what's going on—party or something?'

'Oh well, be reasonable—they've got to clear up, haven't they? Mrs. Fraser does most of it herself I believe. Mr. Fraser won't have Alec working in the bars at all, any time.'

'Did you know he was friendly with Susan?'

'Oh yes, I knew. No harm in it. You'd better get across and fetch her back though. And we must have a few words with that young lady.'

When Mr. Prone pushed open the saloon bar door, he was surprised to see ten or a dozen patrons of the Rose and Crown sitting at tables drinking and chatting, though three of them could conceivably have been singing. And among them were his daughter Susan and the licensee's son Alec Fraser; both of them, he reflected grimly, schoolchildren of fifteen. The licensee, Jock Fraser, greeted him with controlled warmth.

'Hallo—Mr. Prone, isn't it? Bit too late, I'm afraid, Mr. Prone.'

'I don't want a drink, thank you. I'm looking for my daughter.'

By this time, of course, the usual silence had taken over as all eyes were turned upon him. The eyes jointly expressed, as is customary in English pubs, the slightly fuzzy hostility reserved for the unknown visitor (Mr. Prone was no pub man); and they might have induced a less agitated person to back out again and shut the door. Even as it was, he noticed that two men folded their arms on their table in an ineffectual and incriminating effort to hide their drinks. This, combined with Mr. Fraser's reference to the time, induced Mr. Prone to look round the bar for the clock and, having found it, to stare at it fixedly for long enough to deepen the surrounding atmosphere of uneasiness.

It was Alec Fraser who spoke up.

'All right, Dad,' he said to the licensee behind the bar, 'this is Mr. Prone's daughter, you only know her as Susan. She's a friend of mine.'

Mr. Prone crossed quickly to where they sat, pulled out a chair and sat on its extreme edge to begin a muttered exhortation.

'I don't know what you think you are doing here', it began.

'I've been having a drink with Alec. He's my boy friend.'

'What's in that glass?'

'Lager and lime.'

'But it's all right,' Alec explained, 'it was ordered before eleven o'clock.'

'I don't care if it was ordered last week', said Mr. Prone. He grabbed the half-empty glass, took it across to the bar, and held it up in front of Mr. Fraser's face.

'Did you supply this drink to that child?' he demanded. He knew he was doing this theatrically, and that it was a nervous reaction to what seemed to him the silent and slit-eyed scrutiny of the assembled company. But if any eyes present were indeed operating through slits, the next development brought them all wide open with a perfectly synchronized click.

The door opened and P.C. Flynn walked in.

'Leave your glasses where they are, ladies and gentlemen', he said loudly. 'It's twenty minutes past eleven and you are all drinking after hours. Permitted hours for drinking intoxicants finish at eleven o'clock, plus ten minutes drinking up time.[1] I shall be wanting all your names and addresses, please, before you leave, and the particulars of what you have in your glasses. . . . Hallo Mr. Prone, I *thought* I saw you through the window. Better start with you, shall we, because we know each other and all I need to find out is what's in your glass.'

And as a preliminary, P.C. Flynn turned and shot both bolts in the saloon bar door, by way of hindering any rapid exit.

Mr. Prone was in a position of some delicacy. If he disowned lawful connection with the glass of lager and lime in his hand, he would thus proclaim himself as a man who not merely picked up other people's drinks when they were not looking but did it after hours. If on the other hand he disclosed that it was Susan's he would be accusing her of two offences: drinking after hours[2] and (being under eighteen years old) 'consuming intoxicating liquor in a bar'.[3] Nor would it be self-evident that the drink was Susan's, since he was holding it, she was sitting at a table, and he was the only person standing at the bar.

'It's a lager and lime,' he said slowly, 'and you know my address.'

So it was Susan who broke the angry silence among the customers.

'That's not his', she called out indignantly. 'You leave my father alone. That's not his drink, it's mine, I was drinking it, and I had it before he came in, before eleven o'clock. He came here looking for me and he's just taken it away from me. You leave him alone. My name's Susan Prone and I'm fifteen and if you know where he lives you know where I live too.'

Mr. Prone shrugged and put the glass down.

'This ought to crown your police career', he said to P.C. Flynn. 'Think of the headlines! NIGHT PUB SCHOOLGIRL: SINGLE-HANDED CAPTURE. Would you like me to alert all the crime reporters?'

But P.C. Flynn had moved across to a group of gin-and-tonic consumers at a table, one of whom suddenly became loquacious.

'Listen mate,' said the gin-and-tonic, 'I'm allowed to drink this for half an hour after closing time, I don't know where you get the ten minutes from. That means half past eleven, and we haven't got there yet. You've got it all wrong mate.'

P.C. Flynn was writing the date on a new page in his notebook. 'The

[1] Licensing Act 1964, section 63(1)(a).
[2] Ibid., section 59(1)(b).
[3] Ibid., section 169(2).

half hour', he explained, 'applies only when you order the drink at the same time as a meal. What meals are you serving?' he called to Mr. Fraser.

'I don't serve any meals at all', said the genial custodian of the Rose and Crown.

'Not even sandwiches?'

'No call for them.'

'I see. Well, then, the half-hour exemption isn't much use to anyone here, is it? Name and address please, sir? Perhaps a driving licence?'

'I think you might give me a chance to say something,' Mr. Fraser interrupted loudly, 'me being the licensee of this place. Do I get a look-in?'

'No one wants to stop you, Mr. Fraser.'

'Well, these people are all friends of mine, all guests, and they're all drinking at my expense.'

P.C. Flynn's pencil stopped in mid-air. At this point he had to be careful,[1] if possible without betraying the fact.

'I see', he said. 'Mr. Prone and his daughter, they're old friends of yours?'

'Friends and neighbours. Just across the road.'

'That's nice. What's the name of this gentleman sitting here?'

'Name? Oh, we just call him Sandy, I've known him for years as Sandy.'

P.C. Flynn looked quizzically at Sandy.

'And yet Sandy doesn't seem to fit any of your names,' he said to him, 'according to this driving licence?'

'It's just a nickname.'

'I see. And you live at Rugby? Just popping in, like, for a quick one before bed-time?'

'I'm on a visit to this lady and gentleman here, they live locally.'

'So perhaps Mr. Fraser could tell me *their* names, at any rate?' said P.C. Flynn.

Mr. Fraser couldn't.

'I don't think it's any good really, Mr. Fraser', said the omniscient Flynn. 'The law says you can't get away on this lark simply by telling your customers that if they stay on you'll treat them as private friends.[2] And you see, if you run this defence about *bona fide* friends, *you'll* have

---

[1] Licensing Act 1964, section 63(3)(b) exempts 'the supply of intoxicating liquor for consumption on the premises to any private friends of a person residing there who are *bona fide* friends entertained by him at his own expense, or the consumption of intoxicating liquor by persons so supplied'.

[2] *Corbett* v. *Haigh* (1879), 44 J.P. 39.

to prove the truth of it. It's the magistrate who decides whether they're sham friendships or real hospitality.[1] I think that's the way it goes.'

And the odious formalities of name-taking then proceeded, in the grimmest of atmospheres, while Mr. Prone, waiting for the saloon bar door to be unbolted, sat at the table with Susan and her escort, who found themselves listening to a monologue of unexampled ferocity. Eventually P.C. Flynn came round to Jock Fraser.

'Do you think Miss Susan Prone looks eighteen?'

'Yes I do.'

'What do you go by?'

'I know what a woman looks like, don't I? She could easily be eighteen, you ask anyone. What do I have to do, ask for birth certificates? You ask her father here, does *he* think she looks eighteen?'

Whether or not his view was coloured by a desire to hamper P.C. Flynn and the smooth course of justice, Mr. Prone said (without waiting to be asked) that he thought she looked more.

'Ask anyone here,' said Mr. Fraser, 'there's a dozen of them, a proper jury, ask *them*—ladies and gentlemen, do *you* think this young lady looks eighteen?'

'YES!' they all shouted.

All of which P.C. Flynn impassively noted in his little book. At last he went to the door and drew the bolts; for such is the docility of the drinking classes, and such the effortless authority of a police uniform, pencil, and notebook, that no one had imagined himself free to go.

'Good night all', said P.C. Flynn, but he might as well have been addressing an empty bar, with all its chairs upside down on the tables.

'Now,' said Mr. Prone, 'late as it is, I want to know what it was you were trying to tell me across the road.' They were sitting uneasily in the shop parlour.

'Come on Susan,' Mrs. Prone said, 'I can see there's something.'

For some time Susan looked at the floor, Mrs. Prone looked at her daughter, and Mr. Prone looked at the clock. Suddenly there came a barely audible trickle of words.

'I thought Alec was going to tell you', Susan began. 'But I suppose there was so much going on. . . . Alec and I are going to get married.'

Mrs. Prone only just escaped falling off her chair, Mr. Prone began opening and closing his jaws in the way that seemed to help him over life's crises. It was accordingly Mrs. Prone who spoke next.

[1] *Atkins* v. *Agar* (1914), 78 J.P. 7.

'MARRIED!' she almost shrieked. 'At fifteen? What on earth are you talking about? Married at school?'

'Plenty of people get married while they're at school', said Susan, who knew of one. 'And there's plenty of countries where a girl can marry at twelve.'

Mr. Prone's voice came back. 'You can't marry without my consent and your mother's. Never mind what they do in other countries. We're in this country', he said at last rather feebly.

'Anyway she can't marry at all until she's sixteen,' said her mother, 'she can't have a legal marriage, whether we consent or not. That's right, isn't it?'

Mr. Prone said it was right.

'If you won't let us marry we're going to live together till we're both sixteen and *then* marry.'

There was another stunned silence.

'What is all this *about*?' asked Mrs. Prone at length. 'Does he think he's *got* to marry you or something—?'

'No he doesn't and he hasn't. We haven't been to bed together or anything, ever. That's what we want to do and we're going to do it properly, all open and above board and no sneaking about behind hedges and sheds and places.'

Mr. Prone had a sudden priceless inspiration. 'But don't you know,' he said, 'you'd both be committing a *crime* if you did that, both of you under sixteen? Have you ever heard of the age of consent?'

Susan was not to know that the girl herself can't be charged.[1]

'Well if that's right I shall find out tomorrow', she said. 'I'm going to the family planning clinic to see about getting the Pill.'

She ran upstairs to her bedroom, leaving the Prones staring at each other in silence, and without even the resolution to make a cup of tea. Soon they too went to bed.

Mr. Prone awoke suddenly to find that it was only 3.15. What had disturbed him? The bedside radio was still on faintly, he decided: she must have gone to sleep and forgotten it. He reached out to switch it off, and found that it was not switched on. He sat up suddenly.

'What's that?' he said nervously. 'Who's that?'

'Eh?' said Mrs. Prone into her pillow. 'What? What time is it? Why, it's still dark.'

'It's someone talking downstairs. No, it's outside. I know what that is, it's a police car radio—'

[1] *R.* v. *Tyndall* (1894) 1 Q.B. 710.

There came a banging on the street door at the side of the shop, and Mr. Prone began putting on his slippers and dressing-gown. 'Who the hell', he added in the angry falsetto of a man who knows and dislikes the answer, 'is this?'

Down at the street door stood two motor patrol constables.

'Have you got a car in your garage?' said one of them. Mr. Prone said he had.

'And is it a Volkswagen estate No. 92BUP62Z?' went on the policeman, to whom that possibility seemed enough to exclude any question of politeness or apology.

'I don't know the number off-hand, I've just bought a Volkswagen', Mr. Prone said.

'Are you Mr. Percival Prone?'

Mr. Prone said he was.

'If that's the number of your car it has been used in an armed hold-up at Caterham, and we'd like you to tell us what you know about it.'

Mr. Prone blinked at them sleepily but angrily. They had just told him all he knew about it. But 'My car is in the garage,' he said, 'my wife put it there when we got home at nearly midnight. I don't know what you're talking about.'

But at their suggestion he took them inside, through the parlour at the rear of the shop, to the kitchen, where an internal door gave access to the garage. The garage was empty.

'And your story is that you know nothing about where it's gone?'

Mr. Prone, too wretched to notice the bit about 'your story', was glaring at the middle of the garage floor.

'Of course I don't. It's been stolen. It must have been done after about 11.50 last night. I was at the police station with it until then, from about ten o'clock, and one of your people had driven it there.' He told them briefly the story of the breathalyser, and they seemed to hear it with some distaste.

'Your wife put it away last night? And did she lock the garage doors?'

'I'll go and ask her', said Mr. Prone, but she was on her way downstairs already. Rapidly introduced to the story so far, she began to look rather shamefaced.

'I didn't happen to put it in the garage', she said with an attempt at carelessness which was badly under-rehearsed. And it came out that, having tried three times to back it into the rather narrow garage, she had decided to leave it round the corner for the night. And there, she said, it probably still was.

Everyone hurried through the house again to the side entrance, and there, sure enough, fifty yards away from the corner, stood 92BUP62Z. Surprise about this was confined to the police members of the party.

'Something's gone wrong', hazarded one of the policemen. By the time it had been agreed all round that something had gone wrong, a radio conversation was in progress between the patrol car and the police station; from which it emerged that the Police National Computer, by which the registration numbers of cars were recorded against their owners' names and addresses, had culpably recorded two different Volkswagens as having the same number. And this, the police were excusably anxious to explain, was not the fault of the Police National Computer but that of the Department of the Environment's Computer Centre at Swansea, which supplied the police with such details on request.

'I don't like it', grumbled Mr. Prone. 'I don't like the idea that there's some other car running around with my number on it. And criminals in it. How do I know that I'm in the clear? Or when do I know?'

By this time the telephoning policeman had learned a little of what may be called the Prone Saga, and was at pains to reassure him. If there *was* another car with his number, he was told, the matter would be cleared up. He was not to worry. He was to go back to bed and get a good night's sleep.

'A good night's—' Mr. Prone gulped. 'Do you know what time it is? Ten to four! I've got to be up anyway at five. Good night's sleep!'

And he was still muttering angrily as his wife propelled him up to bed again with the promise that she would not only get the morning tea but sort the morning papers for delivery.

Friday

HE was a little conscience-stricken about the garage entrance. What made it needlessly narrow was the presence, on each side, of a shabby stone baluster such as you often see outside Victorian villas. Each was surmounted by a stone sphere which (significantly) was about the size of a human head, and was supposed to symbolize the severed heads of deer poachers anciently found within the squire's grounds. But although their original purpose might justify the researches of someone with nothing much better to do, it would (in the case of Spenser Park General Stores) probably disappoint even him. Mr. Prone had intended for a long time to knock them down and then freshly cement the whole drive-in. Two circumstances now combined to suggest that the time had come.

The first of course was Mrs. Prone's difficulty about backing the Volkswagen into the rather narrow entrance. The second was that Mr. Prone had been aware for three or four years that a large heap of sharp gravel, ideal for concrete mixing, had stood uncared for, seemingly unwanted, and apparently ownerless on the empty building plot at the corner of Sandford Hill. He had often thought of going along one dark night with his garden barrow and helping himself, and the thought had recently been revived when he overheard two men in the shop discussing precisely that possibility. The kind of instinct that had hitherto prevented him was the kind which now made it difficult to think of that gravel as ownerless. Perhaps it really did belong to someone? Of course not. It was forgotten, abandoned, it even had weeds growing on it. Anyone was entitled to it. Then why had he always thought of doing it in the dark? Simply because a respectable shopkeeper is not to be seen wheeling barrowloads of gravel about the streets. Did that mean it was respectable to do it when no one could see? Well, Mr. Prone did think there might be legal snags about 'abandoned' property, but in matters of law he was an ignorant man—though he had sometimes thought of mentioning the heap of gravel to Mr. Parrott. Why then had he not done so? Was it because Mr. Parrott might say it would be unlawful to take any? All this suddenly seemed far-fetched and futile. There was always a time for action.

Thoughtfully at 5.30 this dark November morning he put out the empty milk bottles at the side entrance and then stepped out into the street. The yard and garden at the rear of the shop were accessible from the road by a side entrance, guarded by tall and padlocked double doors. Just inside them there always stood a rusty and extremely rickety iron wheelbarrow, kept available for the moving of heavy cartons of Prone merchandise. He opened the doors, stepped inside, and placed a heavy shovel in the barrow; an operation which made enough noise to divert the attention of Mrs. Prone from sorting the morning newspapers for delivery.

'That you Percy? What's wrong out there?' Her inflection carried an unmistakable reminder that there were urgent things for him to be doing inside.

'I'm just getting the barrow out', he called, trying to make that sound a perfectly normal thing to do on a pitch-dark morning.

'*Barrow*? What do you want with a barrow now?'

He put the handles down and reluctantly went in to explain. She listened without enthusiasm, not even looking up from what she was doing.

'But doesn't that gravel belong to the builders?' was her predictably irritating response.

'What builders? It probably belonged to a builder at some time or other, but he's probably gone bankrupt, they're always going bankrupt.'

Mrs. Prone thought of the typewriter ribbons, and sniffed at the suggestion of bankrupt stock. 'Do you know who the builder was?' she said.

'There aren't any builders' boards there, haven't been any for years. No one could prove it belongs to anyone after all this time.' And there began a discussion which, if he weakened now, could turn out to be long and time-wasting.

'I'm only thinking of you,' he said touchingly, 'and about that garage entrance. If I'm going to do it over the weekend this is the time to fetch the gravel.'

If Mrs. Prone was touched, she concealed her emotion effortlessly.

'I don't call this the time,' she said, 'and anyway it will take you an hour—'

But he had gone.

In fact it was only fifteen minutes later that he was unsteadily on his way back, the shovel perched on top of about two hundredweight of gravel, his back straightened by the tension, and his arms feeling twice their normal length. His whole attention was engrossed by the knowledge that a momentary loss of balance would simply deposit the two hundredweight in some place inconveniently more conspicuous than the one he had just left. It was for this reason that the police patrol car had stopped almost beside him without his noticing its approach.

'Where's that going then?' said the young policeman who stepped out to greet him.

'Oh, er, just along the road. I'm cementing.'

There ensued a barrage of questions. Where could you get gravel at 5.45 in the morning? Why wouldn't they deliver it? Did you have to provide your own barrow? Whose barrow was this one? Must have wheeled it a long way—there wasn't a builder's yard anywhere near? Why was it all mixed up with grass and dockleaves? Any extra charge for those?

And as Mr. Prone's answers grew less convincing, so the questions grew more facetious. Was he perhaps selling gravel from door to door? Did people have to supply their own bags? Who did the shovelling? Wouldn't it be easier for him on four wheels, or at least two? At length Mr. Prone came out with it.

'This belongs to nobody,' he said, 'it's been lying in a heap at the corner of Sandford Hill for years and years. Anybody can have it. And I need some for cementing.'

But the policemen knew about the Sandford Hill building site. They thought Mr. Prone had better give them his name and address and then take the gravel back there. The incident would have to be reported, they said, and possibly he would receive a summons for the theft of the gravel.

'You can't call that theft', said Mr. Prone angrily, having declared his name and address. His contacts with the law were now equipping him with a little learning; which, for all that Pope had said about its being a dangerous thing, seemed to him a lot less dangerous than none at all. 'I can tell you two reasons why you can't say that's theft,' he went on. 'One is that nobody owns it—you can't steal from nobody. And the other is that you want me to take it back anyway, so I won't have it any more will I?'

But there was a discouraging silence while one of the policemen wrote slowly in his little book. 'Have you got something on you to prove your identity?' he asked.

'Oh for God's sake,' howled Mr. Prone suddenly, 'go along to my shop, one of you, and find out. I promise not to run away with the gravel—'

'Hullo, Mr. Prone, I thought that was you', said a new voice, a treble one.

One of his newspaper delivery boys, just setting off on his bicycle, had stunt-skidded to a halt. He was not a boy of whom Mr. Prone was specially fond.

'Er yes Reginald, there's a misunderstanding and the policemen are helping me clear it up.'

'Helping you with your inquiries?' grinned Reginald objectionably.

'You know this gentleman do you?' said one of the policemen.

'What, know Mr. Prone? Oh yes, I know Mr. Prone, I do a newspaper round for him, don't I? Don't you know him then? What's the gravel for guv'nor?'

'On your way, Reginald', Mr. Prone said tartly. 'Everything's late as it is.'

And Reginald, standing on his cycle pedals despite Mr. Prone's repeated instructions that he was not to do so, reluctantly swayed off into the dark, while the policemen returned to the subject of getting the gravel back where it belonged.

'I'll walk back with you', one of them said. 'That barrow looks like falling to pieces any moment. Sure you didn't pinch that too?'

Not once had Mr. Prone, throughout this terrible week, felt so close to outright mutiny. An act of sturdy individualism was being degraded into a scene of humiliating slave labour. He ought to refuse to wheel the gravel back to Sandford Hill. He *would* refuse, and be damned to them. What then, though? They would arrest him. Was there absolutely no escape?

This internal dialogue had taken up a little time, and the policemen showed signs of impatience.

'I suppose you're not thinking now of leaving this little lot here, Mr. Prone, are you?' said one of them. 'Because I might tell you this, *we're* not taking charge of it. And we're not taking it back, either.'

But for one difficulty, the policemen might have gone on to explain to Mr. Prone the system by which the police temporarily sequestered property alleged to be stolen, so that it might be produced as an 'exhibit' in court, decorated with a luggage label saying what it was. What stopped them was that no one could really call it a system. Its nearest approach to the systematic was that you produced in court anything that was of convenient size, was inanimate, and didn't stink. If, that is to say, a man was accused of stealing an aircraft, a herd of cattle, a horse, or a load of stable manure, you relied upon the magistrates to extend their imagination, calling upon their experience to provide them with the mental image of an aircraft, a herd of cattle, or a horse, or the more varied sensual impact of a load of manure. In the case of Mr. Prone and the gravel it would be difficult and irksome to get it to court, and difficult also to find a magistrate, to say nothing of a justices' clerk, who would take kindly to the deposit of two hundredweight of weed-grown ballast on the court-room floor, or even to the presence of a barrow containing it. And a 'sample' handful, since it could have come from anywhere, would not be of much probative value. As it was, one of the policemen sketched in for Mr. Prone the pros and cons of leaving his barrow and contents where they were.

'I can't say whether there will be a charge of theft,' he added, 'although you wouldn't stop it being theft by just putting it back at our suggestion. But whether it's theft or not, I shall have to report you for wheeling a barrow on the footway.[1] And of course if you go off and leave it here, there will be an obstruction charge as well.'

Mr. Prone picked up the handles, executed a perilous about-turn that nearly deposited his barrow-load on the pavement, and took it all back, muttering angrily and breathlessly to himself, as he went along, that one day he would show the police how they *ought* to be spending their time in the public interest. The opportunity to do which was closer than he could possibly have known.

'What on earth have you been doing?' asked the distracted Mrs. Prone,

[1] Metropolitan Police Act 1839, section 54(7): 'Every person who shall ... draw or drive ... any barrow upon any footway or curbstone' may be taken into custody without warrant by any constable.

anger swiftly taking over from anxiety. And as he told her he meekly drank the cup of cold tea which had stood waiting for him. Ostentatiously, she made no attempt to make or pour a fresh one; and then he went again to the side door—this time to padlock the yard gates.

He had just done so when, glancing along Norman Avenue, the dark little side street of Victorian semi-detached houses, he thought he saw a man climbing out of a ground-floor bay window, about twenty yards away on the other side. This was not the normal means of egress from the houses in Norman Avenue; but, overwhelmed as he was with his own misfortunes, he was back in the shop before it had established itself in his mind with sufficient clarity to rouse any real curiosity. Then, on a kind of double-take impulse, he grabbed Jimmy's air pistol from a chair in the kitchen and hurried back to the street door. The man by this time was very slowly and stealthily closing the sash window, obviously so preoccupied with the need to do it silently that he was careless as to who might see him doing it at all. Exactly opposite him in Norman Avenue stood the Prones' Volkswagen, parked there by Mrs. Prone the previous night.

Quickly and silently in his plimsolls, Mr. Prone ran to the car, opened the front passenger door and left it open. He was suddenly filled with the excitement of action, galvanized (one can only imagine) by this heaven-sent opportunity to show the police how their time should really be spent, the kind of law-breaking they ought to be looking for instead of persecuting honest shopkeepers.

'Right!' he shouted, suddenly stepping into the middle of the road. 'Stay where you are! I've got you covered', and to make this last phrase (which had just occurred to him) seem more compelling he held out the air pistol at arm's length, shoulder high and carefully aimed.

'Sh-sh, you bloody fool', hissed the burglar, and even in his excitement Mr. Prone knew that this was an untypical and disappointing response. But he was taking no nonsense, no chances.

'Come over here and get in this car,' he commanded, 'and don't make any mistakes—this gun is loaded and I shall shoot. I mean exactly what I say', he added, lest the burglar might be so untypical as to suppose him to have meant something else.

'Now look, I don't know who you are—'

'I don't know who you are either. Come on, in you get. That's it, right in. Mind your fingers.' Mr. Prone slammed the car door and moved round to the front, so that he could observe both front doors as well as watching his prisoner through the windscreen.

'Help!' he then shouted. 'Police! Help! I say, HELP!' he shrieked, and the volume of noise he was emitting staggered even himself. Bedroom windows began to open as the citizens of Norman Avenue settled, elbows on window sills, to watch the drama. None of them seemed disposed to come down and join in.

None, that is to say, except Mrs. Prone, who made a startled and incredulous entry at this very point. She hurried towards the car.

'Percy?' she called. 'What on *earth*—'

'Run back and 'phone the police. 999. Tell them Norman Avenue, don't forget that. I've got a burglar in the car. Quick!'

'Why have you got the headlights full on? Where are you? I can't see a thing.'

Neither, he found, could he. Dazzled by the sudden switching on of the headlights, he dodged to the pavement and found to his dismay that the driver's door was wide open. Nor was that all. There was a wildly running figure in the middle distance, and he realized that his captive had gone. He set off frantically in pursuit, letting off an occasional but increasingly breathless hoot of 'Police!' or 'Stop Thief!', which he had always understood to be the right expressions to use.

He reminded himself, as he ran, that if you were pursuing an adversary and you had a loaded pistol (even an air pistol which made no very impressive noise when fired), you had the advantage so long as your man was within pistol range, or thought he was. Within range, although he might be the better runner, the speed of a pellet made such difference of little account. After that there wasn't much to choose. *Loaded* pistol, did he say? Did he really know it was loaded? Come to that, had not Jimmy been repeatedly told never to leave it lying about loaded? While the chase was actually in progress, there was only one way to find out, and that was to shoot. But he wanted to brandish it rather than fire it; and since it didn't automatically reload and he had no other pellets with him, the firing of a warning shot would be no more than the uttering of an empty threat. Nevertheless, it was plain that brandishing wouldn't do much good either, since by advertising the dramatic presence of a pistol, brandishing would encourage the already marked absence of helpful citizens. He decided to fire a warning shot, making sure that it would go at least twenty yards over the fugitive's head. He fired, and was deeply disappointed at the resulting noise; but with a howl the fugitive clapped one hand to the seat of his trousers, stopped running, and turned ferociously upon his pursuer.

Mr. Prone stopped running too, quickly overcame his astonishment that his one and only bullet should have found so inadvertent a billet, and resumed the long-arm stance with the pistol which (he thought) had formerly looked so threatening and effective.

'Stay where you are', he commanded for the second time in their brief acquaintance. 'Put your hands against that wall. Now don't move.'

And then, for the second time on that dark, eventful morning a police car sidled up and stopped behind him. In his excitement he was unaware of it until he heard its doors slamming. And the two policemen who then appeared were, he at once realized uneasily, the two who had figured in the recent episode with the barrow-load of gravel.

'You again?' said one of them, and his surprise seemed as painful as it was genuine. 'Is that your car along there, with all its lights blazing?'

And at that moment Mrs. Prone had caught up with them.

'Yes, that's our car', she said. 'Percy, what's going on, for God's sake?'

'This bloody maniac', gasped the man, 'has shot me with that gun, you'd all better be careful—he's dangerous.'

'Here's the pistol,' said Mr. Prone rather loftily, 'it's only a child's thing and it's not loaded. I want this man arrested for burglary,' he continued, 'he's just come out of a house across the road there. I caught him climbing out of the window.'

'*Caught* him, did you?' said the policeman. 'How do we know it isn't his own house?'

And while Mr. Prone stared his shocked incredulity, mixed now with sudden apprehension, both policemen turned their attention to the supposed burglar, whose complaint that he had been shot was borne out by a circular red patch on the seat of his trousers. Did he want to go to hospital, he was asked? He did not. And wherever he did want to go, it was becoming obvious that he wanted to go there unaccompanied by policemen. Out came the little notebook. Name and address please?

'I'm not giving my name and address', said the man, who clearly felt he had given enough. 'I've done nothing wrong.'

'This gentleman says you climbed out of a window along the road there.'

'This gentleman', the man explained, 'is a bloody fool, as well as being a liar and a homicidal maniac. I haven't climbed out of anywhere.'

Whereupon the whole party moved along towards the house indicated by Mr. Prone; followed—even accompanied, now that all danger seemed to be past and the police were on the scene—by a growing contingent of Norman Avenue residents, all in various kinds of improvised early morning attire. The wounded man, who seemed to walk without difficulty, went along with a reluctance so obvious that the two policemen walked very close to him, one on each side.

'That's the house,' Mr. Prone announced, when they were opposite the Volkswagen, 'Number 29. He came out of that bay window.'

'And you are quite sure this is the same man?'

'Never took my eyes off him.'

'Well, before we do anything else, will you turn off those headlights? And while you're about it, you'd better turn the vehicle right round— you're parked on the wrong side.'

'It wasn't me that switched the lights on,' said Mr. Prone, 'it was him. I was keeping him inside the car while my wife went to call the police, and he switched them on to dazzle us, then he hopped out and did a bunk up the road.'

'How did you get him into the car?'

'With that', said Mr. Prone, indicating the pistol.

'I see', said the policeman. And then, while Mr. Prone was turning the car round, in obedience to a law which everyone seemed to ignore and of which he himself had previously known nothing,[1] the police officers took the suspected burglar to the front door of the house and rang the bell. They had to ring it several times before it was slowly opened to the extent made possible by a safety chain; and then through the gap they could see a lady in a dressing-gown eyeing them all with unconcealed distaste.

'We're police officers, madam', said the elder of them half apologetic- ally. 'Can we come in for a couple of minutes?'

'You're not coming in here for a couple of anything, at this time of the morning', she snapped.

'This man is said to have been found climbing out of your front room window, and we'd like to see if you can identify him.'

This, it turned out, was not the very best way of approaching the subject. What it lacked was finesse.

'WHAT?' said the lady. 'What do you mean, identify him? Identify a burglar? How many burglars do you think I have in and out of here? Why should I be able to identify a burglar who comes in my house?'

'Betty,' called the man she was asked to identify, abandoning his for- mer pretences, 'let them come in and let's get this settled for Pete's sake. It won't take a minute.'

'Who's that?' she called. 'Get what settled?' But she unfastened the safety chain and they all trooped in, followed now by Mr. Prone. Mrs. Prone, with a shrug, had hurried back to the business of preparing the shop for the day.

'This man claims to know you, madam', one of the policemen said.'I notice he calls you Betty. Does that happen to be your name?'

---

[1] Motor Vehicles (Construction and Use) Regulations 1973, Reg. 115: 'No person shall, except with the permission of a police officer in uniform, cause or permit any motor vehicle to stand on any road during the hours of darkness otherwise than with the left or near side of the vehicle as close as may be to the edge of the carriageway.'

'It *is* my name, yes, but I don't know how he knows it, I've never seen him before.'

'BETTY!' cried the supposed burglar, and if his voice did not express genuine anguish and rejection, it got as near to that as any substitute could be expected to get.

'This is fastened on the inside', called the younger policeman from the window: he had been poking around both inside and outside the house. 'Safety catch is on. People don't usually do that *after* the burglar's gone? I wonder', he said to the supposed burglar, 'if you would lend me your left shoe for a minute?'

Distractedly the man tore it off and threw it to him. 'Betty', he repeated tensely, 'I've been shot. This dangerous idiot thought I was breaking out of your house, took me for a burglar or something. You've *got* to tell them why I was in here.'

Betty seemed totally unmoved by this. 'I don't know who you are', she said. 'I'm sorry if you've been hurt, you look all right to me, but anyway I don't know you from Adam and you have certainly not been in here to my knowledge.'

'Is anything missing from the house?' asked a policeman.

'I don't know. How should I know? I was asleep when you started ringing and banging, I haven't looked. Anyway there's been nobody in here, now will you please all go away? My husband will answer any other questions, he'll be home about midday.'

And it was at that moment that the younger policeman leaned through the now open window. 'Thank you,' he said as he held out the man's left shoe, 'the treads on your shoe exactly fit this new footprint under the window.'

The party then withdrew, left the lady to resolve her own mystery, and heard her replace the safety chain on the front door. Outside, the vindicated non-burglar spread out his hands. 'Listen,' he said, 'I spent the night with that lady. She denies it but I did. So far as I'm concerned that's the end of it. What do you want me to do now?'

'I think you'd better come to the station and get it all sorted out', the elder policeman said.

'It's all sorted out as far as I'm concerned. I don't want to go to the station and I'm not going. I have to catch a train.'

'Never mind about that. You'd better come anyway. We can't settle it all here in the street.'

'Well, I'm just not coming. There's nothing further to settle.'

'You need medical attention, for one thing. You allege you've been shot.'

'What do you mean, allege? Anyway you can leave that to me. . . .

Look here, I'm now going to walk away. And I said walk. I'm not going to run away, because you people always take that as a confession of guilt of some kind. If you try to stop me—'

'Now listen', said the policeman, and he opened the door of the patrol car, which had now been brought back to the scene. 'There are things you can't really decide here. You've got to decide whether to charge this man with shooting you, grievous bodily harm or something. You need to think things over a bit. You ought to have that shot wound attended to. We would like to know a bit more about your movements last night and this morning, and a bit more about the lady and her husband—'

'I daresay you would. Well, I've got nothing more to say and I'm not making any charges against anybody. I don't want anything more to do with all this, and I'm going.'

'Do I have to arrest you then?'

'That's your problem. But I can tell you this: if you do, I shall inform my solicitors and we shall take legal action against you.'

It was quite a familiar police poser, usually to be overcome by persuasion and bluff but this time, it was all too apparent, not to be fitted into any such convenient pattern. The man with the little red circle on his pants (it had grown no larger) was already walking away, and decision had to be swift.

'Let him go', said the elder policeman. 'We'll pick him up somewhere if we want him.' And they both watched his departure like anglers whose lines had snapped. 'We'd better take this one in though.'

This one, Mr. Prone realized, meant himself. Why did they propose taking *him* in?

'Well, there's quite a lot really, isn't there? Wounding with intent to do grievous bodily harm.[1] Carrying a loaded firearm in a public place.[2] Possessing a firearm with intent to injure.[3] Possessing an offensive weapon in a public place.[4] Discharging a firearm in the street.[5] And that only takes care of the air pistol, doesn't it? Whose is it, by the way?'

'It's my son's, and I certainly never fired with intent to hit anybody, that's absurd—'

'And how old is your son?'

'He's nine.'

'Nine, is he? So how did *he* get a firearm then?'

'Firearm? It's an air pistol, a toy.'

---

[1] Offences Against the Person Act 1861, section 18.
[2] Firearms Act 1968, section 19.
[3] Ibid., section 16.
[4] Prevention of Crime Act 1952, section 1.
[5] Metropolitan Police Act 1839, section 54(15).

'It's a firearm all the same. How did he come by it?'

'It was a present to him, if you call it a firearm. Present from an uncle of his.'

'Ah. We shall have to see the uncle then, won't we? You see, your boy being under fourteen, no one can lawfully *give* him a firearm, not even an airgun.'[1]

'You'll be lucky,' said Mr. Prone defiantly, 'that uncle lives in Vancouver.'

'Does he now? We should have to see about that, wouldn't we? Then there's the question of your car and the way it was parked—'

'It wasn't me that turned the lights on.'

'No? You parked *without* lights, then, did you? That's another thing, you see, another offence.[2] It all adds up, doesn't it?'

'But look here, you've got to try and be a bit reasonable about this. You say I parked it on the wrong side of the road. I suppose that's because the side lights might worry anyone driving through? But none of these cars have any lights on in Norman Avenue, or anywhere else for that matter, you know that perfectly well, why pick on me all the time—?'

'They don't all shove themselves under our notice the way you do. Hop in please.'

It would be an abuse of language to say that Mr. Prone actually hopped in, but he entered the police car in a state of exasperation not previously attained at any time during the week. 'You'd better stop at the corner,' he managed to say, 'and tell my wife where I'm going to be.'

And they did. She told them at once that it was she who had parked the Volkswagen with its offside against the kerb; and no, she didn't leave any lights on, no one ever did along that road. How could the lights be dangerous to other drivers if they weren't switched on?

'Nobody's said anything about danger from the lights, Mrs. Prone. If there's any danger it's from not having any lights at all. You simply mustn't park at night with your offside to the kerb.'

'But why?' demanded Mrs. Prone.

'Because the law says so. And at one time it didn't have anything to do with lights on a parked vehicle.[3] This *is* Mr. Prone, is it, madam? Just verifying, you see. Seem to have heard about you quite a lot lately, Mr. Prone. Perhaps we'd better be getting along?'

---

[1] Firearms Act 1968, section 24(2)(a).

[2] Road Vehicles Lighting Regulations 1971.

[3] It began life as the Emergency Powers (Defence) Standing Vehicles Order 1940, at the height of the London blitz. It was born of the 'black-out', but it had little to do with dazzle for approaching drivers. In the pitch blackness of moonless nights, the rear reflectors on cars were the only indication to an oncoming driver that a vehicle was in his path.

Mr. Prone, however, had been thinking. As an object lesson in the art of challenging arrest, what he had just witnessed in Norman Avenue was conveniently fresh in his mind. He cleared his throat.

'Are you quite sure you understand what you're doing?' he said to the elder of the two constables. It was intended to sound threatening.

The policeman made it clear that he did. 'I'm arresting you,' he said, 'for wounding with intent to do grievous bodily harm, and for possessing a firearm with intent to injure.'

'All right, then I want to talk to my solicitor.'

'We will call him from the station.'

'Just what I thought. And when we get there, you'll say we'll call him a little later on. And then a *lot* later on something will have cropped up to make it seem undesirable to call him for a little longer. Well, we'll call him from here.' He caught his wife's eye. 'Ring up Mr. Parrott right away, will you?' he said. 'He's got a 'phone in his bedroom.'

And at that moment Mr. Prone acquired an unexpected ally.

'Look, mate,' muttered the younger constable uneasily to his colleague, 'I think this is a non-starter. I mean it's a lot of rot.'

'You WHAT?'

'I don't think any of this will stick. I mean if a bloke shoots a kid's air pistol up into the air, I don't think that's shooting with intent to hurt. And if he reckons he's seen a burglar climbing out of a window, well I don't see how you can blame him for picking up some kind of weapon. First thing that comes to hand like.'

'Not if it's out of *his* window, no. This was a burglar coming out of someone else's, or he thought it was a burglar. Turns out he was wrong, doesn't it? That chap wasn't burgling anyone, he was after crumpet, not crime. Anyway I suppose you're not saying he *imagined* he was shot in the backside?'

'The thing is, he won't prosecute, he wants nothing to do with it. All you've got against this man is firing an air pistol in the street, and this business about possessing an offensive weapon. They're summonses: we *know* where he lives. As for wrong-side parking, that was his wife, and that's another summons. I don't reckon this is a proper arrest.'

'I say it is.'

'Well, I'm sorry, it's not an arrest by me.'

Mr. Prone was a fascinated listener to this unexpected dialogue, taking place at the very door of his shop and seeming, for the moment, to ignore his existence; or at least to have relegated him to the status of A or X in an examination question. He must, he decided, try to remember every word for transmission in due course to Mr. Parrott. But he affected not to be listening.

'You've left it a bit late, chum', said the elder policeman. 'This man has been taken into custody, by *both* of us. You can't release him now, any more than I can, without the authority of a superior officer.'

'So I've heard. Well, now, we'll just see how that works in practice. I say this is an unnecessary arrest. Not unlawful, unnecessary. Here the man is, in his own shop, not likely to run away over a daft affair like this, a right storm in a teacup. And anyway he was trying to enforce the law like a good citizen. If you're taking him inside, you're on your own.'

'Look, it's nearly time to knock off. What are you going to do?'

'I'm walking. You carry on by yourself if you want to take him in. And you're dead right, it's nearly knocking off time, so I'm starting now. See you later.'

And the younger constable set off on foot for the police station.

'If it's nearly time for you to knock off,' said Mr. Prone to the remaining policeman, 'you're going to be unlucky, aren't you?' He was getting to know the inner anguishes of police routine. 'I mean you've got a lot of writing to do before you can go home?'

And then Mrs. Prone's unerring sense of dramatic fitness came to life.

'Perhaps,' she said, 'he'd like a nice strong cup of tea.' And, with an almost visible slump into relaxation, he said he would.

'Of course,' he said, 'I shall have to take the firearm in. And then you'll hear a bit more about that.'

'You keep calling it a firearm', objected Mr. Prone. 'It's an air pistol, that's all it is.'

'It's not allowed for kids, all the same, not under fourteen.[1] And it's unlawful for anyone to give it to the boy. That'll have to be looked into as well.'

'All right, but I didn't give it to him. I told you, it was his uncle, he was here on a visit from Canada last year.'

'The trouble is, Mr. Prone, you're probably liable for aiding and abetting both offences, the boy's and his uncle's.'

'What do you mean, the boy's? I've already been told the boy's too young to commit *any* offence.'

'Ah, um, yes. But I reckon,' said the officer, under the mellowing influence of Mrs. Prone's tea, 'it *might* be dealt with by a caution. You won't get the firearm back though, I shouldn't think. I'd better be going—I'm bound to report a lot of all this.'

The policeman stood up and put on his cap. 'I'm not very happy about not taking you inside', he said. 'There's a lot to be cleared up

---

[1] Firearms Act 1968, section 22(4): 'It is an offence for a person under the age of fourteen to have with him an air weapon or ammunition for an air weapon.'

about that non-burglary business, and it's not really for me to clear it up. Still, you don't look as if you'll run away.'

It was now half-past seven and getting light. Susan appeared, in a neat skirt and blouse, and began setting the table for breakfast: as an opening scene for the next Act, it could hardly have been more conventional. Seemingly oblivious of what had been going on, she nevertheless peered uneasily through the shop as the police car departed.

'What did that policeman want, Mum? Did he say anything about me?'

'About *you*? Why on earth should he say anything about you? The police don't come round inquiring about girls not going to school, that's nothing to do with them. Besides, you're going to school now, all that business is over.'

'Oh well, it wasn't really that.'

Mrs. Prone looked her up and down, head on one side. 'I suppose you're going to tell me that wasn't your father's drink in the pub last night? Well I know it wasn't, everybody knows that—'

'No no, nothing to do with that.'

'Come on then. Out with it.'

'It's something I didn't tell you about, Mum. It happened about a month ago.'

There was a silence filled with apprehension and guesswork. It was broken by Mr. Prone. 'If', he said, 'it's something more about this boy Alec Fraser—'

'It's not really to do with him, except he was with me when I found it.'

'Found *what*?'

'We were coming out of the Wimpy Bar that evening and I kicked something along the corridor. There wasn't much light just there and I thought it was a little empty carton of some kind, we couldn't see it at first. And then I thought it wasn't a carton and started to look for it, I don't really know why. And when we found it, well it was this bracelet.' And to stem their flow of questions, Susan ran upstairs and came down with a heavy silver Victorian bangle, which she placed on the kitchen table. Mr. Prone picked it up.

'You can't *keep* a thing like this', he said, turning it over in his hands. 'It's silver, solid silver. Valuable.'

'I know it is,' said Susan miserably, 'but at first we thought it was just one of those things you can buy in Woolworths. I know you're supposed to take things you find to the police station, but there must be *some* things too soppy to take. We thought this might be worth about 20 pence.'

'You should take *everything* to the police station', Mr. Prone said sternly.

'Oh come off it, Percy', said his wife. 'Like what? Pencils? Evening papers? Bus tickets?'

'Well, you've done nothing about it at all?' he said, ignoring this contribution.

'One day I was looking in Sanders's window and I saw one just like it and it was £48! So I didn't know what to do, Alec said keep quiet about it. But then I had an idea, I took it to another jewellers, along the Neville Road, and they said it was worth £40.'

'Oh, and did they want to buy it?'

'Not very much, I don't think. I thought perhaps he was wondering how I got it or whose it was.'

'If he'd wanted to buy it,' said Mrs. Prone decidedly, 'he'd have said £20, not £40.'

'So why have you kept quiet about it, Susan, all this time?' demanded her father.

And Susan explained that she and Alec Fraser had begun to look upon it as a possible nest-egg, an omen perhaps; a sign that their marriage might be blessed, and the beginnings of a bottom drawer. With every day that then ensued, it became more difficult and (she rather supposed) more dangerous to reveal their secret. And now it was too late she didn't know *what* to do.

'Who says it's too late?' said her father.

'I do', said Mrs. Prone firmly. 'If she takes that to the police now they'll say she's stolen it. They'll make a great thing of it the moment they hear the name Prone.'

'How the devil can they say she's stolen it when she's giving it up to them?'

'They'll want to know why she's kept it a month and why she's suddenly decided to turn it in. And then they'll say she *attempted* to steal it, or something like that.'

'Nonsense!'

'No it isn't and they probably won't even believe she found it, they'll think she stole it from somewhere. They'll make inquiries at all the jewellers, and that one in Neville Road, he'll say, "Oh yes, a schoolgirl came in with it", and they'll find out it's her.'

'But can't you understand, she'd never go to a jewellers or the police if she'd stolen it.'

'She could steal it from somebody, say from a ladies' room while someone was washing their hands, and then wait a couple of weeks to give the owner a chance to tell the police. And then when she goes to the station they will be able to tell her whether it's been reported stolen or lost. If it hasn't they've got to hand it back to her after a time, two or three months I think it is, and everything legal and above board. If it *has* been reported, then she gets a pat on the back and perhaps a reward from the owner.'

Susan was gazing at her mother open-mouthed. Mr. Prone wasn't really listening. 'What I'll do,' he said, 'I'll put a notice in the shop window. "Found, heavy silver bangle or bracelet: Inquire within".'

'We don't want to do that either', said Susan slowly. 'Alec wants us to keep it.'

'And after the way the police have been treating us,' said Mrs. Prone, 'I should think they're entitled to keep it.'

Mr. Prone was now angry. 'How the devil can you say they're entitled to keep it? She's made no inquiries at all, except about the value of it. It's not her bracelet, never can be. Suppose it was yours and someone had stolen it or even found it? Would you say they were entitled to keep it? Not you. It may seem a bit late to go to the police, but we can advertise it. I'll put a notice in the window.'

'And it reminds me,' said Mrs. Prone, 'you haven't decided yet what to do about that camera.' Mr. Prone thought he had.

The story of the camera, a poignant one, had been clouding the senior Prone consciences for considerably more than a month. For Mr. Prone it was a portable problem in moral philosophy, he took it everywhere with him. It threw up an inconvenient challenge to a tidy principle in his mind which held that if ever a choice confronting you was a difficult choice, that was because it involved choosing between two evils. A choice between good and evil was simple, Mr. Prone had read somewhere, according to whether you were good or evil yourself. He thought, in a modest sort of way, that morally he was fairly good. Or at any rate far from evil. And yet the affair of the camera was not to be settled along these lines.

It began three years earlier, when Mrs. Prone took the children away for what had turned out to be a wet holiday. (Like so many captive shopkeepers, he couldn't go himself. His wife at one time used to try persuading him to go, but he rather luxuriated in being indispensable.) They took with them a camera which, partly because of the weather and partly because they were not a photographic family, was never taken out of its canvas carrying case throughout the holiday. When they were unpacking again at home it was nowhere to be found. The Prone family had racked its four brains as to when and where the camera was last seen, and they came up with four different answers, all wrong. The holiday landlady was written to, as were the local seaside police, and no news of the camera was ever obtained from anyone.

Now Mr. Prone had a lifelong propensity for losing things, and a few years earlier had been persuaded without difficulty that he should insure against losses inside or outside the household. The required premium was small and the promised relief from worry was large. He now wrote and told the insurance company about the loss of his camera, which he valued at £12, and a young man called to discuss the claim with him. Had he told his own local police station as well as the seaside one? He had. Various possible explanations of the loss were talked over; and in due course the insurance company sent him a cheque for £12.

Mr. Prone was greatly impressed by this evidence of good faith on the part of his insurance company, and went around telling everyone about it; sunning himself, so to speak, in its gratifying radiance. Then one day Mrs. Prone decided to empty out a cylindrical umbrella-stand which stood, rather neglected, by the side door. And out tumbled the long-lost camera. The original details of the camera story were subjected to a shocked and rather embarrassed re-scrutiny. No one could swear to having seen the thing actually put into any of the holiday bags; and it became necessary to admit, with whatever reluctance, that it might have been in the umbrella stand for a long time. No one remembered how it got there.

But what now?

The insurance company were clearly entitled to either £12 or the camera. And as if Mr. Prone's conscience was not capable of solving the problem unaided, the story was known now to a wide assortment of people. Not merely the children and others who frequented shop and house, but the large number of customers to whom he had so happily told the story as evidence of his own business acumen and the probity of his chosen insurers.

He had made up his mind.

'I shall send the company a cheque for £12', he said, and his elbows lifted slightly.

Mrs. Prone's nod was so nearly imperceptible that not many people would have called it a nod.

'I wouldn't do that, if you ask me', said Susan, whom no one had asked. 'That won't do any good. Anyway, they're too big to feel it, they will *never* know anything about it.'

'I think that's wrong,' said Mr. Prone, 'and it's not something you've learned from me. I've made up my mind.' And he turned to the morning business of opening the letters.

Among them all, one envelope claimed his instant if reluctant notice by the legend along the top: COMMISSIONER OF POLICE OF THE METROPOLIS—a phrase which now brought him about the same degree of pleasure as most men get from INSPECTOR OF TAXES. In reply to Mr. Prone's inquiry, said the signatory, he was directed by the Commissioner to inform Mr. Prone that he (meaning Mr. Prone) was no longer a member of the Special Constabulary and that if he was still in possession of any accoutrements issued to him in that capacity he was to hand them in at the nearest police station.

He was pleased about this, for two reasons: the first well founded, the second illusory. Not only had he been unwilling any longer to be an auxiliary member of any police service whatsoever, but he was now at liberty (he told himself) to serve on that jury at the Old Bailey.

'I'll be all right for jury service after all,' he called to his wife in the shop, 'I'm not a Special any longer.'

Mrs. Prone came to the parlour door. 'You soon forget, don't you?' she said. 'You can't serve on any jury for ten years after you *stop* being a Special Constable, and you'd better put it out of your mind. And anyway if you think you could find the time to go off serving on juries, you could have found the time to go away for a holiday with the children— which you've never done. I don't see how you could do either, mind you, but you seem to know some way.'

Crestfallen, he returned to the letters.

His new driving licence was among them. 'I've got my licence at last,' he called, 'but judging from what it says on the back I won't have it for long—I've got motoring summonses on the way that will fill it right up with endorsements, and that'll get me disqualified too.'

'Well,' said his wife, 'you'd better begin by signing it, you don't want to get caught like that again.'

He looked at his new licence. 'Usual signature in ink', he read out. 'What ink? Does that include a ball-point? Have we got a bottle of ink?'

'Oh don't be so silly, of course it's all right with a biro.'

'I'm not certain about anything any longer, *anything*. I reckon I was pretty ignorant about the law at the beginning of this week, but I reckon I prefer it that way. After what I've been through I'll be terrified to fill up the simplest kind of form, everything you do can be wrong. . . . Why, what's all this about?'

'What now?'

'Letter from a solicitor. Says they are acting for Messrs. Higgs and Llewellyn, owners of No. 86 Spenser Road, in the matter of Ancient Lights. Ancient Lights?'

'No. 86? That's the Whiffens next door!'

'Well, they only rent it. They've sold the business I believe, though he never tells me anything himself. He's moving away, the milkman told me. And listen to what these damn solicitors say:

> Our clients inform us that their tenant, Mr. Samuel Whiffen, has repeatedly asked you to lop the branches of the elm tree growing on your land which obstructs the light of two windows and a glass roof at No. 86 Spenser Road . . .'

'Yes, that's true enough anyway', said Mrs. Prone. 'Or it's true about her—she's always on at me about that wretched tree. You can't say I've never told you.'

'Oh that's great, that is. So I've got you to fight as well, have I?'

'Don't be so sorry for yourself all the time. Of course you haven't got to fight me. I shan't say anything about the Whiffens to anyone. All I mean is, if you were thinking of fighting the case and saying boo to these solicitors—well, think again: it's cheaper probably to have the tree taken down. Anyway it's got Dutch elm disease and it will have to come down soon. Otherwise it'll fall down.'

'If it does that it's certain to fall the wrong way and smash his fence or something', said the fatalistic Mr. Prone. 'Anyway I shall take this letter to Mr. Parrott this evening. I thought Ancient Lights was only to do with buildings, not trees.'

By this time a massive dossier of queries for Mr. Parrott had accumulated in the course of yet another of these crowded days; but there was more to come.

By ten o'clock that morning the Prone establishment had been increased by the addition of Sophie to its payroll. Sophie was a plump and cheerful girl of Jamaican parentage, born fifteen years ago in Neville Road and a true child of the neighbourhood. She had responded promptly to Mr. Prone's advertisement in the shop window and was now, as he came into the shop from his letter-opening, looking round for work to do.

'I'll tell you what you can do, Rosie—'

'Sophie', said Mrs. Prone.

'Sophie. I'll tell you what you can do, just give the car a wash-over for me. I'll fetch it round to the front of the shop while you get the bucket and sponge. It's only just round the corner.'

Within a few minutes Sophie was soaking the pavement and roadway as well as the car with soapy water which spread bubbles around in profusion. It was not long before she realized that she was being watched with some interest by P.C. Flynn.

'Is this your vehicle?' he asked her.

'Mine? Don't make me laff. It's Mr. Prone's. I work here now.'

The shop doorbell pinged severely as P.C. Flynn, having told her to suspend operations, went in and began a predictably one-sided conversation with Mr. Prone.

'I am informed', he said, 'by your next-door neighbour that the girl cleaning your car is splashing soapy water on the footway in front of his shop. It's slippery for passers-by and customers, and he is also expecting removals men at any moment; the footway will be dangerous for them.'

The information was received in stony silence by both the Prones.

'Section 54(1) of the Metropolitan Police Act 1839,' went on their tormentor, 'says that you mustn't clean or repair a vehicle in a thoroughfare or public place, to the annoyance of the inhabitants or passengers. I have received a complaint from Mr. Whiffen about it, and I shall have to report the matter.'

Mr. Prone spoke first.

'Did Mr. Whiffen send for you,' he asked, 'or did you just happen to be passing? Don't tell me. Look, will you tell me something else— where do all these people along the road wash their cars? Even if you could wash a car inside a garage, which you can't, there's hardly any of these people have got garages.'

'I'm afraid that's nothing to do with me. I mean I can see your problem, but it's not one that I arranged for you, is it? And nor is it me that can solve it. If I receive a complaint I have to act on it, you see.'

'Even if you go and stir up the complainant first?'

'We shall have to see what the magistrates say, shan't we?'

That always seemed to be P.C. Flynn's personal exculpation. If his own conduct appeared oppressive or officious (and to Mr. Prone it did, though such were not the adjectives that would have contented him), he was a victim of circumstances. There the law was, and there was P.C. Flynn. He had been taught that the enforcement of the criminal law was, with statutory exceptions, the job of the police; and every four-weekly pay day his bank account was officially credited with money extracted from the public under the promise that this was what he would do. If some breach of the law was too trivial for punishment or redress, then it was for the magistrates in their wisdom to say so. That was *their* job, and if they went wrong there were judges higher up to put them right. But they couldn't do their job unless he did his: without him they were helpless ornaments, or anyway helpless. He had heard of 'police discretion', but that seemed to him a phrase used by people who wanted the law ignored until the moment when they themselves were incommoded by it. Once you started that kind of thing, where could you decently stop?

And the word 'decently' was crucial, because P.C. Flynn knew that non-enforcement could be encouraged by bribery. No one could bribe P.C. Flynn; or perhaps it should be said that no one, hitherto, had thought it worth while to make a high enough bid. As it was, the car-washing episode, and the annoyance of Mr. Whiffen as a representative of the 'inhabitants or passengers' in Spenser Road, were not the true occasion of P.C. Flynn's visit to the shop this morning. They were among the little eddies left by the main thrust of his relentless progress.

'I've called to see you about that barrow', he said.

Mr. Prone stared. 'Oh no!' he said, 'not you as well? That's all in the hands of the other lot—they stopped me this morning in the dark, when I had some gravel in it.'

'Where *is* the barrow, Mr. Prone?'

'What? Where do you think it is?'

'Where you left it, I would say. On the building site, corner of Sandford Hill. Did you by any chance leave it full of gravel?'

'What would I do that for?'

'So that you could wheel it away another time, perhaps, when the police were not around?'

'You must think I'm absolutely bonkers. I tipped the gravel out.'

'I felt *sure* you did. And then?'

'Then what?'

'The barrow, you see, was found upside down at the bottom of a crater, twenty feet down. Did you throw it down there?'

'So you *know* I didn't leave it full of gravel?' said Mr. Prone angrily. 'As soon as the policemen had gone I gave it a shove,' he said, 'and then let it go.'

'Not wanting it any more?'

'I don't want the damn thing any more, no.'

'That's what I thought, and it's what I called to see you about. The Civic Amenities Act makes that unlawful, Mr. Prone. It's an offence of "abandoning on any land in the open air" something you've taken there for that purpose. There's a fine of £100. It all comes under Control of Pollution.'[1]

'Is that what you call abandoning it, then? What you've done, you've tricked me into saying I don't want it any more, but that's not the same thing as saying I intend to leave it there.'

'Why didn't you bring it home, then?'

'Well if you must know, by that time it was getting light and I didn't much want to be seen with it.'

'But you were going back for it? I see, yes. How would you get it, Mr. Prone? It was twenty feet down in a steep gravel pit and upside down. Anyone who wanted to get that barrow out would need a crane. I suppose it'll be done by somebody one day, but that won't *really* be you, will it?'

Mr. Prone said it would not. Reluctantly he had to agree that they were discussing an abandoned barrow, and that the act of abandoning it had been his. But as he stood there in his persecuted little shop, contemplating the relentless P.C. Flynn, a sudden thought occurred to him, a wildly shocking one. It had occurred to him before, but he had been dissuaded from translating it into action by the irrational hope that sooner or later some building would collapse on top of P.C. Flynn, or that he might be drowned on holiday or fall down dead. None of these happy contingencies had shown any sign of occurring, and in his moments of reflective sanity, now less frequent than they were, he realized that they were hope-engendered fantasies. The nasty things in this life do not, because you merely ignore them, go away. Their departure must be encouraged, engineered.

Dimly, the distracted little man now perceived that he had reached a crossroad, and his state of mind at this crucial moment necessitates a brief digression. Mr. Prone had read about the bribery of policemen, rather as he would read about a small earthquake in Hampstead; not because he was a devoted reader of the newspapers he sold, but because no newsagent, standing in his shop and folding them by the quire, can help noticing headlines three inches tall. For people not lured on to the smaller type, fuller details of such cases were thoughtfully provided by the BBC as a background for lunch and for tea-breaks. Hundreds of police officers, Mr. Prone understood, had in recent years left the London Metropolitan Police (some of them with a face-saving appearance of volition) because they had been found to have impertinently adopted

[1] Civic Amenities Act 1967, section 19(1)(b): 'Any person who, without lawful authority . . . abandons on any land in the open air . . . any thing other than a motor vehicle, being a thing which he has brought to the land for the purpose of abandoning it there', is guilty of an offence. (Abandoning motor vehicles, or bits of motor vehicles, in the same circumstances is separately dealt with.)

business-fostering methods employed by the great multi-national trading corporations. These, it seemed to Mr. Prone, were able to corrupt people without themselves getting into trouble, because they had to further the interests of their governments and other shareholders in countries administered by lesser breeds who had never heard of Polonius or Kipling's 'If'. Even the smaller fry who sometimes corrupted London policemen—the bookmakers, the pornographers, the drug peddlers and the rest—were seldom headlined as facing criminal charges, hiding from the law, or helping police with their inquiries.

The world of business and commerce seemed to be run, in the great boardrooms, on the basis that every man (in other boardrooms) had his price. Why should the business of the corner shop be any different?

Mr. Prone's mind was taking a lamentable turn. He had always set his face against bribery, even in the form of long-established and superficially harmless customs involving no perceptible distortion in the morality of giver or receiver. The Prone–Flynn confrontation was taking place at the time of year when unsolicited Christmas sweeteners were beginning to arrive at the Spenser Park General Stores: calendars, cartons of book-matches, a crate of mineral waters, another of lager. The faces of men arriving in delivery vans were beginning to assume, here and there, the receptive expression produced at Christmas time by the fusion of happiness and deserving poverty. Very soon people everywhere would be giving and receiving, soliciting and scrounging, begging and bestowing, all under the blanket blessing of the Compliments of the Season. What was *really* behind it all? Surely, reflected the new and grubbier Mr. Prone, in the world of trade and business the recipients were silently undertaking to continue the relationship for another year? Well, I'm not, Mr. Prone had told himself. If he didn't approve of, say, Edwards's Sponge Trifles, no illustrated calendar, no free packets at Christmas, would affect his judgement or deflect his custom. Wouldn't they? No impact at all? Well, he didn't really know. So easy to confuse cause and effect.

Anyway, the inexplicable behaviour of P.C. Flynn over the past few days, the seeming determination to run the Spenser Park General Stores into the ground, suddenly took on an appearance which was at once sinister and comprehensible. Mr. Prone gazed fixedly at his tormentor, swallowed hard, and began a colloquy which, as it developed, seemed to be happening in another dimension where he was a helpless spectator.

'Why do you pick on me all the time?' he asked. 'Thousands of other people break the law. Millions. You spend the whole of your time on me, you leave yourself no time to prosecute anyone else. Don't you ever notice an offence committed by someone else? Doesn't anyone else park in some wrong place, or throw down a cigarette packet, or let his dog run out? What have I done to you?'

'Mr. Prone, I—'

'Come on, what have I done to you, ever?'

'You've done nothing to me. I just take the job as it comes—'

'But don't you see, when all these summonses come up in court, whenever that's likely to be, it'll be *Flynn against Prone, Flynn against Prone*, all the time. My solicitor will be there, he'll defend me in every single case, and as it all goes on there'll be a lot of publicity. Everyone will see it's some kind of vendetta by one bloke against another. Is that what you want?'

P.C. Flynn was writing in his little book. 'The barrow is actually your own property, is it, Mr. Prone?' he said. 'It looked like a contractor's barrow to me, I mean it's not a domestic garden barrow, would you say?'

Mr. Prone looked at him long and hard, while a silence fell between them. And then he made up his mind.

'I'm not a rich man', he said. 'You can see for yourself what this place is worth. If I thought you were the kind of policeman who just wanted money I would have offered you £10 before now, just to leave me alone. I might have thought that was what you wanted. Once you'd taken the £10 I would have you by the short hairs—you would have had to dance to *my* tune. But I can see that wouldn't be enough. I am ready now to pay £100 if you will just go away and forget about me. Just to give someone else a chance to get to know you.' And he swallowed hard.

P.C. Flynn regarded him impassively. 'I suppose,' he said, 'living the kind of life you do, I mean without a great deal of time for leisure, you don't get much idea how far £100 will go these days. £100 isn't much good to me these days, Mr. Prone.'

Then he was right! It was a question of how much! Flynn was inspecting the bait, in spite of the warning that he would be 'had by the short hairs' once he had taken a bribe. It could only mean one thing: there *was* a sum of money, if only it could be computed, that would make P.C. Flynn's short hairs seem long enough to minimize any moral discomfort. He might be induced, at some sort of price, not merely to leave his victim alone but also to accept that for ever afterwards, so far as Flynn was concerned, Mr. Prone was to be immune whatever he did. The latter was now thinking desperately. His future was in the hands of a mindless zealot to whom law-enforcement was as indispensable as breakfast, dinner, and tea; a man to whom the costive language of the

Statutes of England was a system of thought, filling the whole of experience. Compassion, fatigue, boredom, justice, the sense of comparison,
counter-attraction—these would never change him. Money might.

'I'll make it £200', said Mr. Prone in a low voice, thankful that his
wife was not within earshot. Whatever the rightful place of the best of
wives, it was not, at decisive moments, within earshot. He felt now like
the crook that circumstances were combining to make him—the law, its
countless trip-wires, the police, and above all 'the police discretion to
prosecute', a discretion which, it was plain, had gone off duty for a week.

P.C. Flynn seemed not to have heard. He was replacing the rubber-
band round his notebook and generally presenting the appearance of a
visitor about to leave.

'Two hundred and fifty', said Mr. Prone desperately.

'You don't have that amount of money on the premises', said P.C.
Flynn, perhaps by way of a blunt intimation that he was not interested
in cheques, IOUs, or other paper promises that can come home to roost.
But the reason he gave was: 'Or if you have, you're very foolish.'

Mr. Prone said that it was on the premises, but that it would be
neither convenient nor safe to count it out there and then. P.C. Flynn
looked at his watch.

'I'll be back at 2.45', he said, and Mr. Prone could scarcely believe
his ears, attuned though these had now become to the absorption of the
unbelievable.

'Listen my dear,' he whispered excitedly to his wife as soon as the
shop door had closed behind P.C. Flynn, 'we've got him. He's going to
accept money to leave us alone. He's mad, he doesn't see what he's doing. I'd never have believed it. He said he'll come back at 2.45 for the
money.'

Mrs. Prone looked at her husband with her head on one side.

'What money?' she said. 'How much?'

'It'll be worth every penny. We can soon make it good, and there's
no other end to this—'

'How much?'

'Yes. . . . Well, I'll have to see how much there is in the till. And
there's a bit more in my desk locked up—'

'HOW MUCH?'

Mr. Prone moved closer. 'He actually *bargained* with me', he said.
'Well, you could have called it bargaining. Two hundred and fifty, I've
been thinking about it for days, and that's what I thought was about our
limit, our outside limit if we went without a number of things. One thing
I can do—'

'WHAT?'

'Eh?'

'Are you talking about £250?'

'It's going to be cheap at the price. It'll buy off this man Flynn, for a start, but that's *only* a start. It'll buy us out of trouble for good and all, don't you see? No other cop can come taking over where he left off, because I can threaten to give the whole story to the newspapers, the whole business of the past week. Nothing like that has ever happened before and any newspaper will see it's a good story, don't you see? I think I'd offer it to the *Clarion* first, they're the ones who hate the police most. And then there's another thing. All these summonses against me, I've got a list of them here.

'There's the Sunday trading thing,' Mr. Prone began his list, 'the shop-blind, the news-stand outside, there's Jimmy's cycle lamps and his early morning round, and that business about the girlie magazines; there's the tax disc on the car, the windscreen washer, the M.O.T. certificate, the driving licence, all those driving offences (Mr. Parrott thinks I'll hear no more about those but I'm not so sure). There's employing that girl Sheila Best, when she was supposed to be at school, there's Mrs. Prendergast and her silly complaints about Bruno and her rotten chickens; and Bruno having no collar on and running loose in a road where he's not supposed to be; and us selling cigarettes to children, and that business about the packet of sponge trifle, and the summons for starting a bus unlawfully. There's that affair about not recording Tom Drake's accident with the window, and then there's his attachment of earnings, I mean me not deducting the money when I paid him. We may get this summons about not putting the milk straight into the cooling cabinet and the other about not renewing our milk licence—'

'Now listen', interrupted Mrs. Prone. 'A lot of this has got nothing whatever to do with P.C. Flynn or any other policeman, you're talking as if the police did everything. If you pay money to the police, what difference is that going to make to the Health Inspector or the Department of Trade and Industry? You're trying to fool me, aren't you?'

'No I am *not*', said Mr. Prone angrily. 'Flynn's the one we've got to take care of, he's not a one-off pot-shot like all the others, he's a right one-man-band. I'm just going through these to remind us of the mess we're in and the reason I think we've got to do something pretty desperate. There's that complaint about not keeping the cakes covered in the shop, and the notice board about the Jack Russell dogs; and there's your silly advert in the shop window about West Indian girl wanted—'

'If *you* call that silly, what about that daft thing you wrote out? We'll never hear the last of that round here.'

'Then there's that carry-on about registration of business names; and the school fuss about Susan's jeans and her O-level exams, and us parking outside Mr. Parrott's and the ghastly business about the breathalyser—'

'What have you done about that?'

'Done about it?'

'Well I mean you've got a blood specimen in that little tiny bottle, the police gave it to you, aren't you going to get that analysed?'

'What on earth's the good? It's a carbon copy of the specimen they've got. If *that's* over the limit, so is this.'

'But their analyst might be wrong.'

'Well, we'll be seeing Mr. Parrott tonight. . . . Anyway, there's me drinking in the Rose and Crown after hours—'

'That was Susan,' said Mrs. Prone, '*she* says so.'

'It was me. And now comes this affair of the gravel and the barrow; and you parking the car on the wrong side at night; and Jimmy having a firearm (well, *they* call it a firearm) and me shooting it off in the street. There's Susan and the found bracelet, and that beast Whiffen and the elm tree, and then Sophie cleaning the car in front of Whiffen's shop.'

'And it doesn't look as if we've finished yet,' said Mrs. Prone, 'Flynn or no Flynn. That's a police car pulling up outside.'

Which, sure enough, it was. 'I thought it was about time', Mr. Prone said, 'we had another one of those bloody things round here.'

In came a young constable, the chequered band round his uniform cap giving him the appearance of a Scots Guardsman dyed blue.

'Mr. Prone?'

Once again, and wearily, Mr. Prone agreed that he had been so described.

'We have two men in custody for crime and we need your help. Do you remember a man named Pilgrim?'

Mr. Prone did. 'He tried to pinch £100 from me. Stole a cheque-book and then forged one of my cheques to the tune of £100. Got away with it, walked away under the noses of the police. They just *let* him walk away.'

'But he doesn't seem to have got away with it, does he? And as we understand it, he walked away under your nose too. You simply watched him walk out of the Midland Bank, because you were too interested in something else going on at the time. At that stage the police didn't know anything about your cheque-book, Mr. Prone.'

'Well, what about him?'

'As I say, we have him in custody and we want you to come to the station and identify him, and sign the charge of theft and forgery.'

'Oh God no! What are you going to cook up next? Can't *you* charge him? You know all the facts. How am I supposed to run this shop?'

'There is also another man. Do you know a man called James Croft?'

'Never heard of him.'

'Or Zenith Office Supplies?'

'Never—*what*?'

'That sounds a bit more familiar?'

'Is that the man who sold me those dud typewriter ribbons?'

'We think so. That's what we want you to tell us. He's been arrested on another charge, and his house was searched, and we found a lot more typewriter ribbons.'

'Good ones?'

'Good ones *and* dud ones. The dud ones were all made up in tin-foil wrappings, for someone like you to buy.'

'Well, I suppose I've got to come, have I? What happens if I refuse?'

'Nothing much at this stage. We might let the bloke go on bail, to come back to the police station when you've changed your mind, which I *think* you would. If you didn't we should try to get a witness summons at the court tomorrow, or a witness order, to make sure you came to court.'

'And if I said shucks to that?' Mr. Prone had reached the stage of saying shucks to everything.

'I don't know, mate, I expect we get a warrant and arrest you.[1] But you won't be as silly as that. After all, it's *your* money we're looking after, your interests.'

'And so what's the good of arresting me? Anyway *that* doesn't make me talk.'

'Well, if you then refuse to give evidence you can go to prison, you see? You can't expect to just defy the law like that. Mind you, I've never seen it happen, because people are not such twits.'

Mr. Prone decided to go.

It took up less time than he had feared. He was asked to sign charges against both men, who were then finger-printed, put in police cells, and told they wouldn't get bail. Mr. Prone was assured, with an unconscious irony that was to have a special poignancy the next morning, that the Magistrates' Court proceedings would be brief and preliminary, and that his evidence at that stage might not be required. It was little more than an hour before a police car obligingly delivered him back at the shop. The clock said 2.25 p.m.

[1] Criminal Procedure (Attendance of Witnesses) Act 1965.

'You could almost call it funny in a way', he told his wife. 'That chap Pilgrim, as soon as he saw me, he said I'd better be careful about what I was doing. If I was there to make charges against him, he was there to make charges against me. If I was prepared to drop my complaint, he was prepared to drop his. He didn't know *quite* what I was accusing him of, but I would certainly know what he could accuse me of, unless my memory was very bad. And so on and so forth.'

'With the police listening?'

'Oh yes, the same detective sergeant was there that handled the job about the typewriter spools. After a bit, Pilgrim seemed to notice they were grinning all over their faces and then he wanted to know what was so funny. In the end the sergeant told him the story about the so-called typewriter ribbons, and how you and I had been fooled by this other bloke—what was it, Frost?'

'James Croft', said Mrs. Prone patiently.

'Croft. So then of course he realized he'd done himself a bit of no good, trying to blackmail me right there in the station. Made it more certain than ever that even if *I* backed out (which I certainly won't now) the police would go ahead with the forgery and theft cases against him.'

'And what *about* this Croft?'

'Oh, he's charged with stealing and receiving God knows how much office equipment, it seems there are prosecutors from several parts of the country, and the one that concerned me was something called "obtaining money from one Percival Prone by criminal deception". . . . Will you attend to that lady while I get my overcoat off and count that money for—you know?'

A young woman had come into the shop and was waiting at the counter. Mrs. Prone, anxious eyes on her husband, reluctantly went to see to her. 'Can I help you?' she said, and the lower part of her face produced a smile.

The girl wanted birthday cards, and was directed to a corner of the shop where they were all displayed in groups that classified them as to ages (Baby's First, Now I'm Three, So You're Eighteen, 70 Years Young) and relationships (Happy Birthday to Our Dear Mum, or Dad or Uncle or Gran or Sonnie). She became absorbed in the solemn business of selection, not even looking up when the shop door opened and admitted, at precisely 2.45 p.m., the perennially unwelcome figure of Police Constable Flynn.

The Prone–Flynn conversations had reached a stage at which the Prones always waited for Flynn to speak first, even if it was only to say 'good afternoon'; and they seldom found it necessary to reply. That, however, was not the position today.

'Good afternoon', said P.C. Flynn.

'Ah!' said Mr. Prone, hearing his voice and coming from the shop parlour with a fat-looking envelope in his hand. 'We've got some unfinished business?' It is just possible that he supposed this to be a tactful way of indicating, in the company of a stranger, that he was bearing a gift of £250 which must be kept a dark secret. He noticed that the young woman was still comparing birthday cards and he lowered his voice. 'You'll find that's correct', he muttered.

'Correct?'

'I mean it's what we agreed.'

'You'd better remind me exactly what we did agree.' P.C. Flynn made no attempt to speak quietly. Perhaps he couldn't, thought Mr. Prone. Perhaps some people can't—town criers, auctioneers, sergeant majors, policemen.

'We agreed on two-fifty.'

'Pounds?'

'Of course pounds.'

'And the idea was that you should be left alone by the police?'

'By you anyway', mumbled Mr. Prone.

'I'd like to get it clear that the idea was yours in the first place? I mean I didn't walk in and demand money from you?'

'Good Lord no. Entirely mine. You can trust me about that.'

P.C. Flynn reached across and took the envelope. 'I'd like you to lock the shop door a couple of minutes,' he said, 'while I count it.'

'Oh well, of course if you want to *count* it—'

'Well, what do you think? Your wife had better witness the counting, too. Otherwise I can say anything about it, can't I?'

'I was going to say if you want to count it,' murmured Mr. Prone, amazed at the policeman's brazenness, 'you'd better come into the shop parlour.'

'No no, I'd like to be certain no one comes into the shop, that's why I want the door locked. I'll do the counting here.'

The door was accordingly locked. P.C. Flynn moved round to a counter not visible from the street. And to Mr. Prone's anguish, opening the envelope there and then, he slowly counted the fifty £5 notes it faithfully contained. Mr. Prone watched with such concentration that it was only as the fiftieth note was being thumbed that he became aware of another watcher. Standing behind him was the young woman from the birthday-card counter, a chosen card in one hand and a coin in the other.

'This is Police Constable Ellen Williams', said P.C. Flynn, introducing her. 'She has been watching the proceedings, which is what she

came in for. I will give you a receipt for the £250, which I have to take
away with me as evidence, and you will be reported for attempting to
corrupt a police officer in the execution of his duty.'[1]

The colour of Mr. Prone's face quite suddenly matched the bald
circle on the top of his head, and his mouth began opening and closing
rhythmically. For a time no sound took the opportunity to get out, and
then—

'Why, you bloody snake in the grass!' he gasped out. 'You started all
this. You're a—what's it?—an agent provocateur, that's what you are.'

'Oh no', said P.C. Flynn. 'You've forgotten—it was you that started
it. You offered me £100 to go away and forget about you. Remember?
Then you went up to £200. I wasn't prompting you. Right? Then £250.
None of this idea came from me. I just let you run on. Then I said,
"You haven't got £250 on the premises", and you said you had. So I
offered to come back at a quarter to three, and here I am. All at your
suggestion, Mr. Prone.'

'I saw that girl watching you out of the corner of her eye, twice', said
Mrs. Prone angrily, when P.C. Flynn and his witness had gone. 'She
wasn't after any birthday cards.'

Mr. Prone said, because he could think of nothing else to say, 'Well,
she didn't *buy* one. She left it on the counter.'

They were to feel, on reflection, that they had probably attempted the
impossible, that Flynn might even have hoped they would offer him a
bribe so that his Prone casebook might be completed. More than ever,
they looked forward now to the meeting with the delphic Mr. Parrott
which had been arranged for eight o'clock that evening.

'But as far as I'm concerned,' said Mr. Prone, 'this one will be a tee-
total meeting.'

'What you want right now', said his wife, 'is a good strong cup of tea.
I'll go and make it.'

The comfort to be drawn from a good strong cup of tea will often last
as long as fifteen minutes, but this one was permitted to go no farther.
The door opened and there appeared a middle-aged lady wearing a

[1] This was P.C. Flynn's on-the-spot version of the convoluted language in
section 1 of the Prevention of Corruption Act 1906: 'If any person corruptly
gives or agrees to give, or offers any gift or consideration, to any agent as an
inducement or reward for doing or forbearing to do any act in relation to his
principal's affairs or business, or for showing or forbearing to show favour or
disfavour to any person in relation to his principal's affairs or business, he shall
be guilty of an offence.' The maximum penalty is imprisonment for two years
plus a fine of any amount the judge thinks fit.

bulky fur coat and one red shoe. She was brandishing a similar shoe aloft as she entered and advanced upon Mr. Prone, and he, realizing at once that (whatever the reason) she was about to hit him on the head with it, instinctively reached up and wrested it from her grasp.

'I'll show you!' she promised, as she stooped to take off the other one. 'You see this?' She placed it on the counter, rather too close to an open box of liquorice allsorts, which Mr. Prone delicately moved further away. 'That's what it ought to be like,' she fumed, 'and the heel's been broken right off by that broken glass thing of yours outside.'

Mr. Prone compared the red shoes and saw that one of them had lost its heel; and Mrs. Prone came to join the discussion.

'It's lost its heel', she said.

'What broken glass thing?' said Mr. Prone.

'There's a great square hole in the glass,' said the angry woman, 'and the heel of my shoe went right into it and snapped off.'

'She means the pavement light over the cellar', said Mrs. Prone. 'One of those panes has been loose for a long time.'

'Well, I want to know what you're going to do about it.'

'About the pavement light,' Mr. Prone asked, 'or the shoe?'

'About both, I suppose, my good man, but first of all about my shoe.'

Now to Mr. Prone this did not seem the right order of things. His first concern must be to find a way of ensuring that no more heels went through the broken pavement light, and he went out to see what could be done. With the cussedness to be expected of all inanimate things during this week in the Prone story, the square hole left by the missing glass prism was in the farthest possible corner from the building line. Accordingly, until it could be repaired it was a danger to all passers-by and it must be covered. With what? He called to Sophie to bring an empty orange box, and he stood guard over the hole until she arrived with it; not unaware that, during the interval, the wrath of their visitor might be exhausting itself upon Mrs. Prone inside. Then, back in the shop, he found that Mrs. Prone was still deeply involved in altercation.

'Twenty-five pounds?' Mrs. Prone was saying. 'If you paid anything like £25 for those things, somebody must have seen you coming.'

'They're genuine Picadors and brand new,' raged the woman, 'and unless you choose to pay for them here and now I shall inform my solicitor.'

'Well,' said Mr. Prone, in a soothing voice that he found some difficulty in producing, 'we should have to talk about that, shouldn't we? We should have to see. I mean first of all, did anyone *see* what happened?'

'See what happened?' said Red Shoes. 'I hope you're not insinuating that I'm making all this up?'

'Tell you what, Mr. Prone,' said Sophie, her black face glowing with good will, 'shall I try and find the heel off the lady's shoe, it must be around some place?'

'That's a good suggestion', said Mrs. Prone. 'If it's not outside it *must* have fallen through the hole into the cellar, and I've only just cleared out that place. Come on Sophie, we'll go and look.'

'And if it's not to be found,' Mr. Prone said slowly when they had gone, 'that looks a bit odd, doesn't it?'

'I don't know quite what you mean,' said Red Shoes, 'but are you trying to say that a woman would go out wearing two shoes but only one heel, in the hope of being able to blame the damaged shoe on someone else? You must be quite mad.'

'If you had another pair of shoes in your bag,' Mr. Prone said, 'it wouldn't seem quite so mad, would it? Mind you, I'm not suggesting anything—'

'Oh I know all about what you're suggesting. Well, you can see what's in my bag'—and she shook out on to the counter the entire contents of her shopping bag; among which, Mr. Prone noticed, there were no shoes. At her suggestion she and Mr. Prone then went outside again to see whether the red heel might after all be lying in front of the shop, bearing silent witness to the mishap. It was not.

Nor was it in the cellar, Mrs. Prone came up to report.

'Bit awkward, isn't it?' Mr. Prone said.

'It's nothing of the kind', retorted Red Shoes, in the tone of a woman who thought it most awkward. 'But I shan't stand here to argue. I simply want you to say whether you propose to pay me £25 for this perfectly new pair of shoes.'

'Not on your nelly', said Mr. Prone. 'I think you've got to prove what you say has happened, and certainly you've got to produce the heel.'

'Then you will be hearing from my solicitors, and your behaviour is quite disgraceful. How do you suppose I am to walk like this?'

'Break the other heel off', said Sophie brightly, a suggestion which did nothing to advance the cause of race relations. 'We can do that for the lady?'

'The least you can do', said Red Shoes, ignoring the cheerful Sophie, 'is permit me to use a telephone and call a taxi.'

It was the fact that she did call a taxi, and did go away in it, that the Prones finally found worrying. 'I don't like her, but I reckon that was a genuine story', said Mr. Prone. 'We shall probably have her solicitor's fee to pay now, as well as the twenty-five quid for the shoes.'

'Nonsense,' said Mrs. Prone, 'there's no need whatever for her to buy a new pair of shoes. Any shoemender can put on another heel like that for less than a pound. The thing is, what are we going to do about the broken pavement light? That's dangerous.'

'I can cut a wooden square for that,' said Mr. Prone, 'chamfer it off and tap it in from the top. I've done it before, it does all right for the time being.'

'Well, I reckon you'd better call that the very next job. If you hear a crash outside in the meantime, it'll be P.C. Flynn falling over our orange box.'

'Or pretending to', said Mr. Prone.

'I'm glad you came early,' Mr. Parrott said, 'I see there's quite a lot to talk about and I don't want to be up too late. I'm off to Brussels early tomorrow.'

'Coming back when?' asked Mr. Prone anxiously.

'I simply can't say. My partner Mr. Grainger has got extremely interested in your case, and he will be available all the time—'

'It's not the same. I don't want anyone else. It's not an ordinary problem. If some of these damn summonses come up while you're away, what do I do?'

'Oh, I shan't be more than a month anyway. None of them will get on for six weeks or so. Months, more likely. Don't worry. And maybe a lot of them won't end in prosecutions at all—I'll tell you the ones that probably will, looking at this tremendous list. This Sunday trading thing, about selling a pack of cards, well, you'll get a letter of caution about that. Or *if* there's a prosecution I'll raise such a stink that you'll get about a thousand pounds' worth of good publicity, and more Sunday customers than ever. Actually if there *was* a conviction I'd like you to appeal, preferably to the High Court, I'm sure we could cook up some sort of a ground. Then this shop-blind—well, that's a bit different, public safety and convenience involved, the thing *ought* to be eight feet from the ground, you see; there no real defence. Not much use saying you didn't know, even if you didn't. You can only plead guilty. You'll have to pay the cost of the summons, it won't be much.'

'Nobody ever told me anything about eight feet', grumbled Mr. Prone. 'That thing's the way it was when I had it put up. What's the date of the Act— 1847?'

'Town Police Clauses Act 1847.'

'So if it's unlawful now it was unlawful when I had it put up, eleven years ago.'

'I daresay, but if you go on like that you'll be almost inviting them to make it into what they call a "continuing offence". If it was, you could

be liable to a forty shilling fine for every day of the eleven years. What's
that?' There was a short silence while they both figured on the backs of
envelopes. 'About £8,000, I suppose', said Mr. Parrott.

'We ought to add these all up,' Mr. Prone said bitterly, 'just to make
it clear to the police that they've really discovered a corner shop being
run by the Rockefellers or Charlie Clore.'

'It's much the same with the stall outside the shop', said Mr. Parrott.
'I see no defence about that, only mitigation. Mitigation on the ground
that so many others do it and never get into trouble; and perhaps that
yours is a special kind of convenient service to the public, which I'd say
it is. . . . Then your son's cycle lamps, that's an offence of "permitting".
He can't be prosecuted himself. Too young. I must say I don't think
this one will come out too well, Mr. Prone. Employing a little boy of
nine on a paper round?'

Mrs. Prone spoke up defensively. 'He *begged* to do it,' she said, 'and
it was only for a couple of weeks. The regular boy was away ill.'

'Ah. Well, we shall plead not guilty and contest that one. *Might* get
away with it. But that brings us to the girlie magazines, I think? The
police are not in on this one?'

'It's a private prosecution', Mr. Prone said. 'Some man to do with
public morality, he thinks Sunday football and indecency are the same
thing.'

'Are these magazines indecent? Have you brought them with
you?'

'I haven't got copies, no. I only ever carried a few copies of such things
anyway, just so as I didn't have to tell customers I didn't stock them at
all—you lose custom like that. I thought the whole affair was daft, and
I can't believe we shall hear any more about it.'

'We shall have to get copies of them.' Mr. Parrott wrote down their
names and dates of publication. 'I think I told you the Indecent Advertisements Act deals with every sort of display or exhibition or publication, besides what one usually calls advertisement. I notice that even the
Law Commission thinks it applies in quite a general way.[1] But it seems
to have been forgotten about. All the moralists and the fig-leaf fusiliers
complain about the law being "powerless". Well it isn't powerless. This
1889 Act is simply a sleeping dog that's been allowed a very long nap,
God knows why. Someone was sure to stir it up sooner or later. We

---

[1] Law Commission Working Paper No. 57 (1974), *Codification of the Criminal
Law, Conspiracies Relating to Morals and Decency*: 'It may be that the Indecent
Advertisements Act 1889 was originally directed against advertisements for
quack remedies for venereal disease, for which other statutory offences are now
available, but the wording is general, and is not even confined to advertisements.'

must try to find out who and what this man is, and whether he's just enforcing his own brand of morality or working for a morality movement of some kind.'

'And then we can bring witnesses to say the things are not indecent?'

'Can we? I wouldn't be so sure. I'm thinking of what I've seen displayed here and there. Saying they're not *obscene*—that's one thing. But indecent simply means Not Decent, and if society decided all these girlie magazines were "decent" I suppose we should all gradually change our way of life quite a bit. One thing's quite sure: the other side would try to stop us calling witnesses about that, because the Act this man is using doesn't allow for it. It's entirely a matter for the magistrate, they will say, without any witnesses. And there's plenty of authority for that, but I'm not sure it's sound authority or that that particular submission has *ever* been right. But I'm afraid this is going to be another difficult one, Mr. Prone.'

So was Mr. Prone. 'All right, then we won't let the magistrates deal with it, we'll demand trial by jury.'

'Nor, I'm afraid, can you even do that. The maximum penalty is only £20 or a month, and that's too small to confer any right to jury trial. No, we shall have to think about this one, and see whether it's worth while taking it to the Crown Court by way of appeal later on. Now what's next? . . . Oh, the tax disc. Now that's what they call an "absolute" offence—the thing is either exhibited or not, and it's either in the right position or not. No argument. We plead guilty on that one and say we didn't know. It'll be mixed in with a lot of other traffic matters—the driving licence, windscreen wipers, driving while uninsured (I don't like that one much), defective handbrake; they might add up, I'm afraid, but the total fines on them all would probably be less than if each one was a solo effort. Anyway, they would all come up on the same day, if the police did go ahead with them.'

'I thought you told me they wouldn't?'

'I think I told you on Tuesday that they'd only just realized some of the traffic offences had been committed while the policeman was sitting in the car with you and directing operations. The inspector I was talking to seemed to think that made prosecution absolutely out of the question. I'm not so sure he's right, and of course the final decision won't be for him to make. I don't *think* you need worry about that particular batch of offences. . . . But now about employing this Sheila Best, I'm afraid you must have been pretty casual about that? I mean did you see her birth certificate or not?'

'I didn't, no. I kept asking her to bring it along, and she kept promising but never did.'

'She looked more than school age?'

'I'd have said so, yes. I'm fed up about that girl, she was a dead loss anyway.'

'She told you she was what age?'

'Sixteen. My wife certainly believed her, and she knows about these things.'

'You could have taken her for eighteen easily', said Mrs. Prone.

'And you never paid employer's National Health contributions for her?'

'We didn't, no. And of course she didn't pay any herself—she never got a card.'

'Very well,' said Mr. Parrott, and to the Prones it seemed an over-statement, 'now what about Bruno? How about him?'

'Well, I used to try keeping him in,' said Mrs. Prone, 'but you've no idea how difficult it is. My husband has never really taken much interest in Bruno—I don't blame him for that, mind you, but it's me that mostly looks after the dog. Since that trouble with Mrs. Prendergast, and that P.C. Flynn coming round about Bruno being loose in the street, well he's been chained up in the yard most of the time, it's awful really. Cruel.'

'I think if you could come to court and talk to the magistrates like *that*,' said Mr. Parrott, 'it might be a lot better than anything I could say to them. What about this selling cigarettes to Mrs. Prendergast's little girl?'

'Little girl!' sniffed Mrs. Prone. 'She's a right baggage, she is. No one would think *she* was under sixteen.'

'But you actually knew her, didn't you? I mean knew who she was? Yes. So you'd know she was still at school with Susan?'

'Well what of it, Mr. Parrott? She doesn't have to be under sixteen for that.'

'Fair enough. How about the date on that packet of sponge trifle? Do you usually keep an eye on those prescribed dates of sale?'

'The truth is we don't need to, they come and go so quickly. You see if somebody came in for a thing we'd stopped selling some time ago, say because there was no demand for it, well then if there was some of it still in stock we'd have a good look at the date on it. But that's about it.'

'I see. I shouldn't think that shows enough care. We must be ready with a rather better story than that, in case a summons *does* come in. I don't think this particular complaint will be pursued, except that you might get an official caution. . . . But then we come to this unfortunate story about your bus journey to the Rotary Club that evening. You seem to have done two things wrong there. You refused to give your name and address to the conductor; that's one offence,[1] I'm afraid, though you subsequently gave them to a policeman. And you unlawfully gave the driver of the bus a signal to start. No defence to those, I fear, only mitigation—I can certainly emphasize the aggressive and cantankerous way the conductor behaved. Pity you have no witness as to that.'

'Oh, the policeman saw all that, I mean he'll know about the state the man was in. And the sort of conductor he was.'

'Provocative?'

'Awful. I could have slugged him.'

'That', said Mr. Parrott, 'is important. I mean important that you didn't. I can certainly ask the police officer what he thought about the man's demeanour.'

'Well, I could see that the bobby didn't think much of him.'

'Now what can you tell me about Tom Drake and his accident?'

Mr. Prone recounted the tale of the broken window sash and his correspondence with the Department of Health and Social Security on the subject of Tom Drake's temporarily flattened fingers.

'The complaint against you will be', said Mr. Parrott, 'that you failed to keep a record of the accident as required by the Social Security Act. I mean required of you as the employer. No answer to that, I'm afraid. Whenever the law alleges a failure to make some record, or the absence of a licence or a permit or some such document, the onus is on the defendant to prove that the record or the document exists. You can't do that, so it's mitigation again. Mind you, there are special circumstances about the employment of this chap, an ex-prisoner you were trying to help—I'll make what I can of that.'

'But the chap from the Social Security said I'd be prosecuted for not producing it, as well as for not having it. They surely can't do that?'

'Unfortunately they can. They tend to try both, in case one charge or the other comes unstuck for some reason they can't foresee; and then sometimes they're surprised themselves that there's a conviction on both counts. I should contest that strongly of course: it's contrary to Natural Justice.'

'What's that?'

'Natural Justice? Oh well, the rules to be followed by judges in settling disputes or trying offenders—fairness, good faith, no bias, giving each side a hearing.'

'Just what I thought. Starts a bit late for me, doesn't it? I mean those rules don't do anything to protect the likes of me against a bloody maniac like this Flynn. Who made them up anyway?'

[1] Public Service Vehicles (Conduct of Drivers Conductors and Passengers) Regulations 1936, Regulation 12(b).

'What we call the Natural Law derives', said Mr. Parrott rhetorically, 'from God, reason, or nature, as distinct from man-made law. A down-to-earth American judge called Oliver Wendell Holmes said it wasn't "a brooding omnipotence in the sky" but a flexible instrument of social order depending on political values.'

'Cor', said Mr. Prone irreverently.

Mr. Parrott coughed. 'I think', he said, 'we'd better move on. . . . You hadn't renewed your milk licence, I believe?'

'There's that and the crate of milk not being put in the cooling cabinet.'

'You'll get a caution about those, I imagine. Prosecution would be most unlikely unless you openly and continually flouted the law. And the same with not keeping the cakes covered. Now what's this?—unauthorized advertisements and town planning? Oh, it's the notice board offering dogs for sale. Now that was put up without your knowledge? And you tell me here it was done by your little boy. Well he's too young to commit an offence against the law, so I think you can forget that one —so long as you remember not to do that kind of thing yourself at some future time.'

Nor did Mr. Parrott seem any more interested in the racial discrimination problems posed by advertising for a West Indian shop assistant, or in the registration of business names, or in the fuss about Susan's being educated in jeans.

'Hold on', said Mr. Prone. 'I daresay you're in a hurry to go to Brussels but these things all mean a lot to me. How about that Business Names thing—if that's right I've got to get all new stationery printed?'

'No no, you can get a rubber stamp made and use that till your present stock of letter-paper's all gone.'

'Jimmy can make us one,' said Mrs. Prone brightly, 'with his little John Bull printing outfit.'

Mr. Prone chose to ignore this contribution. Mr. Parrott now moved on to the question of the breathalyser.

'What did you do with that blood specimen? I hope you've brought it with you?'

'No', said the blood donor a little awkwardly. 'It's bound to be the same as the one the police kept, so what's the use of it? Kind of keepsake? Trophy for the mantelpiece?'

'Now that really is most important', said Mr. Parrott almost angrily. 'Could be vital. Send it round to my office first thing in the morning. We *must* get it analysed.'

'I've got it here', said Mrs. Prone. 'I knew he was being silly about it. I put it in my handbag without telling him or arguing.'

'Excellent. Mr. Prone,' said the solicitor, by way of rescuing her from his baleful glare, 'there have been cases—I know of one myself at first hand—cases where the police get their specimens mixed up, and then when the case gets to court they've got even the blood group wrong. It's the end of the prosecution, of course, but there's nothing like being ready with an analysis of the specimen they've handed to you.'

Mr. Prone hoped Mr. Parrott would be back from Brussels before the case came on.

'Oh it won't get on for weeks', said Mr. Parrott. 'Months. They take a hell of a time nowadays.' With the air of a man who had done it often, he put the precious specimen in a little cardboard box and wrote Mr. Prone's name on it, with the date. 'There isn't time at this very moment,' he said, 'but what I'd like you to do as early as possible, both of you, is to write down everything you can remember about that evening, starting from when the police car stopped you. That's most important. Do it tonight. Will you do that for me?'

'No', said Mr. Prone doggedly.

'I beg your pardon?'

'No. I'd had too much to drink. Sherry. I shall plead guilty.'

Throughout the long silence that followed, Mr. Parrott looked at him over the tops of his glasses as he drummed his fingers on the table. 'As you may imagine,' he said at last very slowly, 'I am thinking of the circumstances in which you did your drinking, or what little of it I was able to observe. Had you been drinking before you saw me that evening?'

'Good God no.'

'And you didn't drink afterwards?'

'How could I do that? The cops were on to me before I'd driven fifty yards.'

'So the whole of your intake of alcohol that evening was here, in this office. In your solicitor's office. Your solicitor, it could be said, plied you with it. Do you see what that entails for me?'

Mr. Prone allowed himself an uncharitable, untimely, and mirthless grin. 'I should think', he said, 'you'd get a real rush of clients. Talk about advertising! Cor.'

There followed a ding-dong discussion, taking up much time and gradually fraying Mr. Parrott's temper, despite Mrs. Prone's mollifying assurances that her husband could get drunk on dill-water. With painful slowness, Mr. Prone was manipulated into a different frame of mind (and morals) by the repeated assurance that any court, on convicting him for 'driving with a blood-alcohol concentration above the prescribed limit', would have no option but to take away his licence for at least a year, whatever the fine might be, and of course his licence would be endorsed even when he eventually got it back.[1]

Mr. Prone's thoughts were occupied by the newly acquired Volkswagen.

'But what defence have I got?' he asked miserably.

'I don't know at this moment, we shall have to see.' The solicitor knew much more than Mr. Prone knew about the legion of drink-and-drive Micawbers who, in the history of breathalyser law, had fruitfully waited for something to turn up.

'Now, how about this episode in the Rose and Crown after hours?' he went on. 'That's not like you, is it?'

'He never goes inside a pub', said Mrs. Prone wistfully. 'Never. He'll even hurry past the door of a pub because of the smell of the beer. That was Susan's drink he had in his hand when the policeman came in, whatever he says about it.'

'It was mine', said Mr. Prone doggedly. Not that he specially revelled in self-sacrifice, but he had now said it many times, in different contexts and company, almost by this time believed it himself, and felt that at this late stage it could not be withdrawn. 'It was my drink', he said.

'So you'll be the only one among these dozen customers of the Rose and Crown to be telling lies? Committing perjury, in fact?'

'Eh?'

'None of the others will deny having unlawful drinks, but neither will any of them claim drinks that belonged to somebody else. If anyone thought it worth the trouble you could easily be bowled out, Mr. Prone. The licensee could do it himself. So could the prosecuting solicitor. The whole thing's against you, the whole scene. Whom are you really trying to protect, Susan or the licensee? If you get Susan off by telling this silly fib, you get the licensee off too on this count of serving teenagers. And yet you believe that's something that ought to be stopped?'

Mr. Prone, once again, gave in. He looked at his watch. 'Have we nearly finished?' he said. 'I want to give the dog a run before I go to bed.'

'There's the theft of the gravel. I can only mitigate on that. The theft is plain as a pikestaff, and I'm afraid the circumstances show that you knew it was, or anyway you felt uneasy? And then there's the abandoning of the barrow itself, the offence under the Civic Amenities Act. I'm afraid you've got no real defence to that. Even mitigation will be difficult enough, in view of your original purpose in going there with the barrow

---

[1] Road Traffic Act 1972, section 6(1) and Schedule IV.

at all. Not very persuasive, really, for me to get up and say, 'My client was only there to steal some gravel, and if the police hadn't come along and interfered he would have taken the barrow home?'

Mr. Prone was watching him grimly.

'But then,' went on Mr. Parrott, 'there's this much more difficult thing about having an offensive weapon in the street, and discharging a firearm. You are not allowed to shoot burglars, even if they *are* burglars. And certainly not other people's burglars.'

'But didn't I read not long ago about a man who shot a burglar and the judges said it was quite all right?'

'It has been held that a householder is not bound to retreat before a burglar because that would amount to "giving up his house to an invader"; and he can use "reasonable force" in self-defence. It *has* been held to include using a firearm, yes. But it has *not* been held to include running after other people's burglars and shooting them in the behind. Anyway it looks as though this chap wasn't a burglar at all. That leaves you without a leg to stand on. You emerge as a would-be good citizen behaving like a dangerous idiot.'

Mr. Prone half rose, sat down again, and changed the subject. 'What about this bracelet Susan's found?'

'Ah, the Victorian bangle. I'm afraid it's not enough to put up that notice in your shop window. You ought to tell the Wimpy Bar people, there's no doubt about that at all, they may well have had an inquiry from the loser. And I think you ought to tell the police too.'

'WHAT!' said Mr. Prone. 'They'll be down on us like a ton of bricks, just the sort of thing they're waiting for. Why didn't we report it at once, and so on?'

'Oh well, you thought you knew who the owner might be, or you were going to make your own inquiries first. Save them the trouble. The police can't do anything to you—so long as you don't hang about any longer than this. They can make faces maybe, and say you were a long time coming forward. But you're not *bound* to tell them at all if you think you can find the owner yourself. The thing is, they're the people who can really spread the information. Some other police station may have a report about the thing being lost—might be a police station at the other end of the country. No difficulty about that—take it to the police tomorrow.'

'Susan won't be very pleased', said Mrs. Prone.

'Susan will get it back if it's not claimed in three months. It was found in the public part of the premises—she's got a better title to it than anyone on earth except the actual owner. You tell her what I say. But your final story is the crucial one, Mr. Prone, this really fantastic

one about Police Constable Flynn and the bribery charge. As to which,
I have news for you.'

'News?'

'News of the highest import.' The Prones sat up. Mr. Parrott's long
practice in the law had developed in him the qualities of the impresario,
always keeping his weightiest pronouncement until it was nearly time
for curtains.

'P.C. Flynn', said Mr. Parrott, 'is in hospital under psychiatric
observation.'

There was another long silence, and as usual it was Mrs. Prone who
recovered first.

'*That's* no surprise, I always thought no normal man would go on
like he did, he was like someone you meet in a bad dream and can't get
away from. You try to run away and your great big feet keep on sticking
in mud or treacle. Well!'

'I'll tell you what', Mr. Prone said. 'He's only just beaten me to it.
If it hadn't been him for the bin, it would have been me. What happened? Do you know the story?'

And Mr. Parrott then outlined for them a story which, as it had
reached him, seemed stranger than anything that had happened during
a week made memorable by strange happenings.

When P.C. Flynn had arrived at the police station with his policewoman
witness and Mr. Prone's £250, he had had some difficulty in getting a
hearing. Mr. Prone was mistaken in supposing that he and his numerous
little lawbreakings engaged the whole of P.C. Flynn's attention. For the
past few months, and at gathering speed, Flynn had been making assorted
arrests among the local citizenry, dragging off to the police station a
great number of minor offenders whose arrest was not merely unnecessary but in many instances unlawful. Even where they were technically
lawful, the victims could only have found their way into police custody
at the hands of a man who had learned all his law-books by heart, dimly
understood them, and then gone out of his mind. Thus among the
Flynn victims were a girl he had found leading along the pavement a cat
with a string tied round its neck,[1] a man he had seen carrying a placard
which announced that The Wicked would Descend into Hell,[2] a boy
who had chalked UP THE SPURS on the wall of a church,[3] two youths

---

[1] Metropolitan Police Act 1839, section 54(7).
[2] Ibid., (8).
[3] Ibid., (10).

he had seen knock at a street door and then run away,[1] and a man with his small son who had been observed trying (vainly) to fly a kite in the street.[2] Outraged at the sight of a foreign-looking man getting into a car which had stood empty for an hour on a single yellow line, he had arrested the man and, on being angrily informed that he was the Spanish Ambassador (which he was), wanted to charge him with personation. It was at this point in high-level police discussions about P.C. Flynn that unanimity was reached: something, it was now agreed, had to be done about P.C. Flynn. He had also accumulated twenty-three cases of unlawful arrest, each of which had involved a perspiring station officer in the compilation of a suitable entry in the Refused Charge Book; and eleven complaints alleging what the Police Discipline Code calls Unnecessary Exercise of Authority.

It had therefore become quite usual, whenever Flynn appeared in the station with some struggling victim of his manic jurisprudence, that a semicircle of his senior officers should assemble with their fists on their hips. It was his production of the Prone £250 that effectively brought down the curtain. A police superintendent, having heard his story, ordained that he was to take the money back, return it to Mr. Prone in person, and get a receipt for it. If there was to be a prosecution under the Prevention of Corruption Act, said this exasperated officer, that could only be at the instance of the Attorney-General, who would be apprised of the full facts but who would *not* want to see Mr. Prone's bundle of fivers.

It was at this point that P.C. Flynn violently flung his helmet to the ground, a passionate gesture not unknown among policemen. He had always known, he suddenly shouted, that half his superior officers were corrupt, but even he had never supposed they would be in league with a little twit like Percival Prone. Whether or not the bribery story ever reached the Attorney-General's ears (he continued), he was going to see to it that it reached the Home Secretary's. What P.C. Flynn did not know was that his recent orgy of indiscriminate law-enforcement, and in particular his past week of Prone-baiting, had resulted in a special file of reports whose unmistakable purport was that P.C. Flynn had gone potty.

What therefore moved into action at this stage was the police machinery by which a person who seems mentally deranged is (without being arrested) persuaded or cajoled into hospital 'for three-day observation'. It succeeded with P.C. Flynn, who now reluctantly supposed that he really did need a rest and some kind of treatment; but it is fair to say that if it had not succeeded he would have been arrested as 'a person

[1] Ibid., (16).
[2] Ibid., (17).

suffering from mental disorder and in immediate need of care and control'; a condition justifying any policeman, who thought it necessary in the interests of P.C. Flynn or anyone else, in removing him to a 'place of safety'.[1] It was understood that if he got better and was able to return to police duty, he would return as a member of the mounted branch; an idea that was greeted with wild enthusiasm everywhere except in the mounted branch.

'So now what happens about all those summonses?' asked Mr. Prone delightedly.

'Ah. Well, looking only at the ones that Flynn was involved in, there's the shop-blind,' said Mr. Parrott in the laundry-list voice that people use when they wish to convey how boring life can be for the truly efficient, 'the news-stand, the bicycle lamp, the employment of your little boy on his paper round, Mrs. Prendergast's grumbles about the dog, the dog running loose with no collar, the advertisement about dogs for sale, the drinking after hours in the Rose and Crown, and the bribery. I'm bound to tell you that none of these need be dropped by the police merely because P.C. Flynn is ill and unable to give evidence. Other evidence is undoubtedly available.'

The Prones' faces fell.

'But I think it rather unlikely that any of them will in fact go on, in view of this subsequent doubt as to the constable's mental condition at all relevant times.'

Up came both faces again. But Mr. Parrott had still to be told about Ancient Lights and the elm tree, about the lady with the red shoes, and about the two prosecutions due to begin the next morning—against Pilgrim for theft and forgery and against James Croft for defrauding the Prones over the typewriter ribbons.

'You'd better get that elm tree taken down', said Mr. Parrott, looking at the solicitors' letter about Ancient Lights. 'Higgs & Llewellyn have owned that place for more than twenty-seven years. If someone's enjoyed a right to the use of daylight in a building for twenty-seven years without interruption, and then you come along and interrupt it, he can get damages against you or he can get an injunction, whichever he prefers. Most of them seem to like the damages. . . . As for the heel of the lady's shoe—well, if she can't find the heel her case isn't all that strong, but you must get that hole filled in.'

'He's done that', said Mrs. Prone proudly.

'Really? How?'

[1] Mental Health Act 1959, section 136.

'Oh, I've had to do it before', Mr. Prone said airily. 'It's only tem-porary. Just a little square of wood, you chamfer it down to fit in the socket, and then you put a screw right through it to another piece of wood underneath.' And he held up the small screwdriver which, as he often did, he had left in his pocket.

'And I went down the cellar,' said Mrs. Prone, 'and held up the other bit of wood till the screw came through and took it up tight.'

'Excellent. . . . Now, I can't help you about these two court cases in the morning,' said Mr. Parrott, 'if you don't want my partner to act for you.'

Mr. Prone repeated that he did not. 'I'll do it myself', he said. 'I know exactly what happened.'

'That may be what *you* think', Mr. Parrott said. 'A very great deal can go wrong in such a case. And in the matter of the typewriter ribbons you do not, if I may say so, come before the court in snow-white raiment. After all, you did think they were genuine ones, didn't you, and despite their very low price you asked very few questions about them? You could *try* to get the hearing adjourned until I'm back from Brussels, but I—'

'You don't even know when that's to be.'

'True enough. They wouldn't adjourn it more than eight days, especially as neither of these chaps looks like getting bail.'

'I'll manage on my own', said Mr. Prone doggedly, mightily encour-aged now by the disappearance of P.C. Flynn from his horizon; a new Mr. Prone, so much less ignorant than a week ago, so full of resolution.

Bruno greeted them with contorted enthusiasm.

'What's that he's got in his mouth?' said Mrs. Prone. 'Oh no!—is that one of our polonies? I got those for our supper.'

'Bruno!' said Mr. Prone sharply, and caught him by the collar. 'This', he announced, 'is not a polony. It's the missing heel.'

'Never? Off that woman's shoe? He must have found it in the base-ment then?'

A silence fell, a fully occupied one. And then—

'Well,' said Mr. Prone, 'what do we do now? Tell Mr. Parrott at once I suppose? Makes all the difference to the case, doesn't it?'

'Oh nonsense Percy, really', said his impatient wife. 'He'll be in his bed by this time, he's off early in the morning, you know that.'

Another moral dilemma. Tell Mr. Parrott about the lost-and-found shoe heel, thus handing to him the problem of whether to keep quiet about it? Throw it on the parlour fire and tell absolutely no one? The slow-combustion fire was still aglow. Mr. Prone reached for the poker.

Bruno watched sadly, head on one side, as the flames licked round the long red heel and destroyed evidence that would have been invaluable, though possibly not vital, to the forthcoming claim by Red Shoes. The flames destroyed, at the same time, some of the lawyer-and-client mutu-ality that the law so jealously protects against the outer world (whatever trouble is thus entailed for third parties). Thoughtfully, Mr. Prone changed into his plimsolls and took down from its kitchen nail the stout new dog-chain he had bought after the encounter between Bruno and Mr. Goodenough's ginger cat. 'I won't be more than ten minutes or so', he called to his wife, who was already busy with the supper.

Of all the miscalculations and false prophecies into which The Week's adventures had betrayed him, this was the gravest and, as it turned out, the most pregnant with dramatic promise.

Panting with pointless excitement, Bruno tugged Mr. Prone along Spenser Road towards the park. He was a powerful dog, his only weak-ness being an innate belief that, once he had made up his mind which way he proposed to go, everyone else would wish to go that way too; and until Bruno had worked off the preliminary delight of an evening walk, Mr. Prone always found himself progressing in a kind of backward-leaning fox-trot. It was one of the reasons, you may remember, why Bruno's old strap had had to be replaced by a strong chain. Spenser Park was of course closed for the night, but Bruno remembered a place where the park railings were bent and a determined Labrador could just wriggle through. He towed Mr. Prone rapidly towards it and within seconds they were on opposite sides of the railings, Bruno jubilant, Mr. Prone spluttering with anger.

'Bruno!' he said sharply. 'Come out!' He pulled and tugged at the dog-chain, Bruno dug in his front paws; and after a prolonged tug-of-war the collar slipped over Bruno's head and he was free, dashing away into the blackness of the park. Whistling and calling through the railings evoked no response. Nor did the flashing of Mr. Prone's electric torch—usually, if oddly, effective in the past. What on earth was a man to do now? Leave the damned thing there and go home to supper? It couldn't get out anywhere else, and the gap made by the bent railing could be closed by twisting and fastening the dog-chain round it. Good God, man, she'd be frantic, you wouldn't get any supper: she'd leave every-thing and go out at once to find her beloved Bruno. Anyway was he *sure* the wretched animal couldn't get out of the park? No, he suddenly realized he wasn't: there *was* a way out—at the back of the head-keeper's lodge half a mile distant along the railings. But, reflected Mr. Prone, if Bruno could leave the park by way of the head-keeper's garden, Bruno's master could get in by the same route. That was it. He would go in and find the dog—who, once he was bored, would always come towards the light of the torch. Then he could grab an ear and lead him back to the dog-chain.

He wound the chain round the gap in the railings and set off for the keeper's lodge.

The trim little house seemed to be in total darkness. No point in knocking the keeper up. His day's duty over, he could hardly be expected to leave his telly and hunt in the darkness for a lost dog. No need to whistle or make any noise, either. If Bruno was still in the park he would see the torch eventually and, having had his fling, he would surrender. . . . By this time Mr. Prone was behind the house and, greatly daring, was letting himself into the park through the keeper's garden gate. He heard a footstep on the gravel.

'Anything wrong?' inquired a policemanly voice, and Mr. Prone turned to see two uniformed constables closing in on him. Up on the road he could see the lights of their patrol car. And this, he decided in something like despair, was about all that was needed to put the finishing touches to a truly hideous week.

Patiently he explained about Bruno's escape, the use of the electric torch, and the corroboration they would find in the shape of the dog chain looped round the park railings. While they listened, he saw the lights come on in the lodge, and then the back door opened.

'Hallo Mr. Stenton,' said one of the policemen, 'we got here as soon as we picked up the message.'

'Very smart work', said the park-keeper. 'What's he up to?'

'Just trying to find out. Perhaps you'd care to tell me', the policeman said to Mr. Prone, 'why you are wearing those sneakers?'

'Sneakers?'

'Plimsolls.'

'I always do of an evening.'

'And carry a torch?'

'When I'm out with the dog, yes.'

'And you're saying this dog is so highly trained that he comes running when you flash a torch in the dark, and yet he's so badly trained that he slips his collar and runs away?'

'Can't you understand, he was excited at first, we'd only just come out. And it was a new collar, too loose for him I suppose.'

'I see. Well, if we went back to the place where you say he went through the railings, we should find the dog-chain tied up there, shouldn't we? And that would lend some weight to your story?'

'I was going to suggest it', said Mr. Prone. 'That's all I want.'

At this point the park-keeper spoke again. 'I suppose you won't need me any more then?' he said.

'Not just now, Mr. Stenton. Later on at the court perhaps. Thanks for the call—looks as if it might be useful.'

'No, that *can't* be the place', said the now desperate Mr. Prone. 'It looks exactly the same, someone's bent the railings open to make a wider gap, see what I mean? There must be another place just like it. Nobody would bother to undo a dog chain tied there, and take it away?'

'That's the way I was thinking', said the policeman. 'We'll drive along slowly and see if it's anywhere else.'

It wasn't.

When Mr. Prone arrived at the police station he saw with mixed feelings that it was the one in which he had taken part in an identification parade, so long ago, so far away. That was last Monday evening. He was invited to turn out his pockets and the screwdriver came to light. As it lay on the table beside his torch, pocket wallet, keys and money, it looked (he thought) positively evil. It convicted him without effort. He hated the look of it. A policeman turned it over in his hands.

'Is this part of the dog-training act too?' he said.

Mr. Prone's story of the job he had done that day with the little screwdriver seemed to interest the police more than he had expected. They wanted to know where the shop was, what kind of shop, whether it had a telephone number. He had already made up his mind not to tell them; he would tell them nothing, absolutely nothing. Never again, whatever the consequences, would he declare his name and address to a policeman. They could all go to hell, he decided.

'You can all go to hell', he said.

A uniformed inspector appeared. 'If you simply took your dog out for a walk,' he said shrewdly, 'you obviously live somewhere close at hand. Isn't there anyone at home who will want to know what's happened to you? Or is there some reason why you don't want the police calling at your home?'

'I don't live far away,' Mr. Prone said, 'but I'm not going to have my wife worried about this or any more police calling there—' He could have bitten his tongue off. What on earth was he saying?

'Any *more* police calling there?'

Mr. Prone was silent.

'Why do they keep calling there? I'd like to know about that? What have the police been up to?'

Silence.

The policemen exchanged what are usually known as significant glances, and after a little policemanly muttering one of them was deputed to 'take him to the Detention Room'. It was a quarter past ten, the polonies would have been ready for a whole hour.

'What's going to happen?' demanded Mr. Prone.

'Well, they'll be framing a charge against you now', said the young constable guarding him.

'Framing, is it? You did say framing? I'm damned if that isn't just what I thought. The whole thing's framed from beginning to end. What sort of charge? Burglary or something? I tell you I've done absolutely nothing wrong—'

'I didn't say that sort of framing, I mean composing, it's all got to be worked out and ready for the formal charging.'

'I see. And that's when I get bail?'

'I'd say you won't get bail at all unless you tell us where you live.'

And at this Mr. Prone became once more obstinately silent. Half an hour later he was taken back to the charge room, where he stood with a large policeman on each side of him and listened, with open-mouthed incredulity, as an inspector delivered the following address in a voice that might be fairly described as that of a Town Crier who was not really trying:

'You are charged that you, not being at your place of abode, had with you an article, to wit a screwdriver, for use in the course of or in connection with a burglary or theft, contrary to—'

'Oh come off it', yelled Mr. Prone, for whom this kind of thing had lost all the majesty that anyone might ever have supposed it to have. 'I've told you about the screwdriver, it was in my pocket by oversight—'

'Will you be QUIET!' rapped the inspector. 'That offence is contrary to section 25(1) of the Theft Act 1968.' And, back on Town Crier level, he resumed:

'You are further charged with being a suspected person loitering in a place of public resort, to wit Spenser Park, with intent to commit an arrestable offence, contrary to section 4 of the Vagrancy Act 1824 as amended by the Criminal Law Act 1967, Schedule 2.'

'And so that's what you've all been framing', said Mr. Prone. 'That's all you could do?'

'Wait, wait', said the inspector, who seemed anxious that Mr. Prone should not speak until some chosen moment. 'There is a further charge:

You are further charged with being found in an enclosed garden, to wit the garden at the rear of The Lodge, Spenser Park, for an unlawful purpose, contrary to section 4 of the Vagrancy Act 1824.'

'Any more?' said Mr. Prone.

'I want you to listen to this caution and not say anything until I've finished—'

'How am I to know when you reckon you've finished? Do you caution people in a special kind of voice or something?'

'Listen to me *please*', said the inspector almost pleadingly.

'Do you wish to say anything? You are not obliged to say anything unless you wish to do so but whatever you say will be taken down in writing and may be given in evidence.'

Then came a pause, which Mr. Prone took to mean that he could now say something if he wished to do so. 'What do you mean,' he said, 'I'm not obliged to say anything unless I *wish* to do so? Even if I do wish to do so, I'm not obliged to, am I? I wish to tell you you're a lot of bloody twits, but I'm not obliged to, surely?'

In spite of his promise, the inspector seemed to make no effort to take this down in writing. 'These are charges', he went on, in a slightly more conversational key, 'in respect of which we take the fingerprints of persons accused. You are entitled to object to that, and we are not empowered to take your fingerprints against your will. Do you have any objection?'

Not only had Mr. Prone an objection, but it was of the kind he had grown accustomed to making at the top of his voice. He was still making it when he found that he had been removed from the inspector's presence and locked in a cell.

'I've got a bit of found property here that might interest you, sir', said an elderly constable, making his appearance for the first time. And he held up Bruno's new chain and collar.

'What the devil's that?' said the inspector impatiently, looking up and glaring over his spectacles. 'Dog chain? . . . Oh, where was it found then? Don't tell me it was on those park railings?'

'That's just where it was, sir. Young couple brought it in about an hour ago.'

'H'm. Better show it to the prisoner, see if he identifies it. No, half a moment, leave it here, let him describe it to you without seeing it.'

But it was not long before the next interruption. A young police-woman looked in and said, 'There's a Mrs. Prone at the Inquiry Desk.'

'Is that so?' said the inspector, without looking up. 'Well?'

'She thinks we've got her husband here sir. She says he went out this evening with the dog, about three hours ago, and she's worried about him.'

'With a *dog*?' Pause. 'I'm a bit worried about him myself now. Show her in, will you?'

Mrs. Prone's distraction could be judged from the fact that she still had her apron on.

'Ah, Mrs. Prune?'

'Prone. I want to inquire about my husband. You see, what it was, the dog came home without him and without any collar or anything, so *something* must have happened to him. So I 'phoned them at Brook Road police station, they know him very well there, and they told me they didn't know what had happened. But the CID, they started 'phoning round and then they called me back and told me there was a man here that might be him.'

'Did they? What time was this?'

'Half an hour ago, and I drove straight here. Is he hurt or something? Do tell me what's the matter please.'

'You'd better come and see the man we've got in the cells, I think.'

'In the CELLS? Whatever for? It can't be anybody who's in the cells.'

But it was. Through the heavily-barred cell gate the indignant and ill-used Prones contemplated each other for nearly half a minute without finding speech. This scene, this climax, crowned the Prone week. This was the point, you could see it now, to which everything had of course been leading. This was Prison, her man was in Prison. The Law at last had got him where it obviously wanted him. Behind Bars.

'Percy!' cried Mrs. Prone. 'They can't do this to *you*! They can't put you in there!'

'No?' said Mr. Prone bitterly. 'Then where the hell am I?'

'Do you know this man?' the inspector asked, as if with a flash of insight.

'This lady's my wife', Mr. Prone said. '*She* will tell you about the dog, and the torch and the screwdriver and everything.'

And she did. Identities were quickly established. The Spenser Park General Stores were called into the discussion and duly acknowledged. 'So they know you at Brook Road?' said the inspector.

'Brook Road police know me very well', Mr. Prone said, without realizing that Brook Road police thought they knew him even better.

'I'll have a word with them', the inspector said. 'Come this way, madam, perhaps you'll wait in there a few minutes'; and the agitated Mrs. Prone found herself once again in a police waiting room. Within minutes the inspector was back.

'Brook Road CID are coming over', he said. 'They'll be here in a minute or two. How did you get here?'

'I brought the car, it's outside. Can my husband go now?'

'I think we're just trying to arrange bail.'

Bail? What on earth did *that* mean? Was he still to be tried for something then? Was there something she hadn't been told about? Whatever had he done? She was soon to learn. The Brook Road men greeted Mr. Prone like an old friend.

'Why Mr. Prone, you again? What is it this time? Suspected person, eh? You're going from bad to worse, aren't you mate? Housebreaking implements? Never known anybody get bail on that kind of ticket before.'

But the discussion that then ensued was concerned with something more than a mere release on bail. Two or three of the officers present thought the whole thing should be dropped, all the charges cancelled, and Mr. Prone sent home. Others, fortified by news (brought by the Brook Road contingent) of Mr. Prone's week of crime, thought differently. He had been formally charged, they said—an irrevocable status in many a policeman's mind, a stigma from which a man may be cleansed only in a court of law. He was in the Wrong Book. You couldn't make a Refused Charge of him now. There was also Mr. Stenton to consider; Mr. Stenton in whose garden this man had been found on a dark night with a screwdriver, a torch, and rubber shoes, telling a story about a dog that seemed not to exist.

The latter view prevailed. Mr. Prone was told that he would be released on bail 'in his own recognisance of £50', that he must be at the Magistrates' Court at 10.30 in the morning, and that he could now go home. Sullenly he signed an undertaking that he would be in court at the stated time; and he took Mrs. Prone's arm as they turned to go.

'Oh, hang on', called the elderly constable. 'Hadn't he better sign for the dog chain and take it?'

'And don't forget,' said one of the Brook Road men as he did so, 'we also need you in court as witness for the prosecution against Pilgrim and Croft. Looks like being one of your busy Saturdays.'

Both Pilgrim and Croft, after formal evidence of arrest, were remanded in custody for further inquiries. Mr. Prone was not called and, sitting at the back of the court-room among people who could not know that he was still a 'suspected person', he saw no more of Pilgrim and Croft than the backs of their heads. The back of his own head, he reflected, would soon be presenting a similar spectacle for the entertainment of that seedy morning assembly of nose-picking watchdogs through whom this country proudly maintains its tradition of 'open court'.

'Number five, sir, Percival Prone!' called a jailer with a clip-board and the voice of an auctioneer. And he had taken us all back to the opening of Chapter One.

Acts, Regulations, and Cases Cited